Model Four Stroke Petrol Engines

Model Four Stroke Petrol Engines

Designing - Building - Running

L.C. Mason

Model & Allied Publications
Argus Books Limited
14 St James Road,
Watford, Herts, England

Model & Allied Publications
Argus Books Limited
14 St James Road, Watford, Herts, England

© L. C. Mason 1976
ISBN 0 85242 431 0

First published 1976
Second impression 1977

Set in IBM Press Roman by
Type Practitioners Ltd, Sevenoaks, Kent.

Printed in Great Britain by
The Garden City Press Limited, Letchworth,
Hertfordshire SG6 1JS

Contents

Introduction

Innumerable model petrol engines have been built over the years, and the greater proportion of these have probably been built from published articles and designs.

This was rarely possible in the really early days of model petrol engines, when a builder had to start from scratch and work out his own design before getting on to the workshop end of things.

This still applies to a much greater extent to four-stroke engines than it does to two-strokes. Not only are there a great many two-stroke designs available, but there are even more to choose from among engines produced commercially. This is not the case with four-strokes, where there are fewer designs and an extremely limited range of engines available to purchase. For this reason, those people who favour four-strokes are much more likely to have to build one for themselves to meet a particular need. For those people who would like to build a four-stroke to include some of their own ideas but are perhaps not too clear on just how to start, or whether a given feature is a good idea or not, then it is hoped that this book can usefully bridge the gap between the purely theoretical "It-can-be-shown-that . . ." type of book, and the "Do this, do that" workshop manual.

There is very little pure theory to be found in this book, and the design points brought out are all treated from the practical standpoint. As in a practical workshop too, the reader may even find a smile here and there!

Two things have been omitted from this book. One is all the elementary explanation of how an I.C. engine works. It has been assumed that someone who is interested enough in petrol engines to want to dig a bit deeper into design points, or to actually build one, will already have a reasonably good knowledge of the "whys-and-wherefores". The other thing is any guidance at all on two-strokes, apart from passing references.

Those people much more interested in four-strokes than two-strokes must also include those interested in modelling old or present day prototypes, for the sake of possessing a working example of an interesting engine, and for them it is hoped that they will find some design or constructional points mentioned which will make the book worth while for them too.

1 Designing in General

When it comes to the actual construction of a model—not only a petrol engine, but any model—you can start almost anywhere in the majority of cases. Several things can have a bearing on where you actually do start; the availability of castings or other bought materials, the point to which a series of articles on it may have reached when you do decide to start, or even, let's face it, the state of the bank balance!

In designing a model, the same thing applies to a large extent. This may perhaps sound a little surprising, when a design is normally taken to mean a complete and detailed whole. Perhaps an outline of my own procedure might show how this comes about, and serve as something of a guide to someone who may be wondering just where and how you start.

In the case of petrol engines, sooner or later I get bitten with the idea that I would like to build an engine of a certain type. This may be for a variety of reasons; perhaps because one like that has not been dealt with very fully before (as was the case with Mastiff), maybe because its diminutive size makes it something of a challenge (as happened with the 4 c.c. 4-cylinder engine), or perhaps just that I would like to introduce some of my own ideas into a more conventional type of engine. Whatever the reason for wanting to build another one, there are nearly always some points or features that you would especially like to include—and these could be your starting points.

I nearly always have a rough scribbling pad handy, and find this invaluable for doodling on while sorting out ideas on odd points—often while supposedly looking at T.V. ! Apart from the special "personal" features of the engine, you will have a rough idea of what the whole thing will include and what it will look like. By this, I mean that you will already have settled that it is going to be say a 10 c.c. O.H.V. job, air-cooled, and of such-and-such bore and stroke. This rough specification outline immediately gives you several dimensions and boundaries which you must keep to throughout, otherwise your design becomes something quite different to what you had in mind.

As with building a model, you can start the actual drawing of the engine almost anywhere, but with petrol engines I always start at one of two places; the cylinder head or the crankshaft. Either of these starting points leads quite naturally to all the rest of the engine, which is not quite the case if you start somewhere else. My drawings run in three stages, when once I have it clearly in mind what I want to do. The first stage is pretty much a freehand sketch, showing the main points of the "special interest" areas, to make sure that it can all be worked in reasonably harmoniously and will not look too outlandish. Clearances between components and whether or no various items can be accommodated in the space mentally allotted to them can all be roughly checked at this stage. If anything shows up as unexpectedly impossible—and it does happen!—this is the stage at which to correct it, or amend some other part of the whole to make it possible. This is the stage too, at which, if it all goes right first time, you get quite excited about it and start thinking "three-dimensionally" for most of the time from then on.

Stage two is a repeat of stage one, but somewhat more precisely, with occasional dimensions beginning to creep in for important parts and with more detail shown, like the location of screw holes with perhaps lugs to accommodate them, that could be taken for granted in stage one. Stage two drawings are valuable, as they are the stepping stones from the rough idea to the finished design drawings, so never on any account throw one away until the whole of the finished drawings are complete. It is still not too late at this stage to alter and drastically modify things. Indeed, if there is any doubt about the feasibility of anything at all, this is the time to get it sorted out. Here in stage two, you will find it desirable to make drawings of several different views, again to check clearances, thicknesses, and feasibility in general. This quite often shows up something getting in the way of something else that had been overlooked in the preliminary rougher sketches, and now is the time to correct things like that too.

Stage three is the final workshop drawing. If you have done a good job with stage two, these stage three drawings should be very little different to the stage twos. I generally build the job right out from the stage three drawings, which in my case are largely undimensioned. Sometimes I find that some little thing may be improved by making it very slightly different, when the actual thing is held in the hand and it does not look quite right. The stage three drawing is dimensioned accordingly, to the preferred dimension of the actual component involved, and so I have an accurately dimensioned record of what I actually did. In the case of a constructional project for "Model Engineer", I then make properly dimensioned drawings from the stage three set, incorporating any odd modifications found desirable along the way. For a "Model Engineer" project, this is necessary, if only because the drawings I have been using in the workshop are by this time distinctly the worse for wear! It is unnecessary to copy the stage three drawings for a project of one's own, of course, and even if they do show a few oil spots or tears at the edges, they could still serve to lend to friends. I have tried photo-copying these for the sake of having a fair copy, but there are some drawbacks to this, and on the whole it is hardly worth it for a personal "one off" project.

A little way back I suggested that the crankshaft or the cylinder head were good places at which to start something like a complete view of the thing. This is a good way to start the stage two drawings. On the whole, I prefer to start off at the crank-shaft, with an end elevation. Here, you can show various circles representing the diameter of the crank throw, the inside dimensions of the crankcase to clear the big end, the length of the conrod, and other essential basic dimensions.

Start with a fair sized sheet of paper and draw in a long vertical centre line. Run a second line across this at right angles to cross the vertical line about a third of the way up from the bottom, and the cross-over point will be the centre of the crankshaft. Draw in the crankshaft diameter circle and the crank pin diameter at Bottom Dead Centre. From these, you can establish the overall width (or diameter) of the bar needed for the crankshaft, from which the circle showing the outermost diameter of the crankshaft swing can go in. Decide on the shape and size of the big end and draw this in place round the crankpin at the bottom.

The big end needs to be treated wtih some respect on paper; if it is split, it will probably come out to something like a rectangle. If it does, it will NOT describe a circle when it is rotating. As it is likely to be wider than it is deep, the smallest cavity that will accept it to swing freely will be a near ellipse, with the vertical minor axis only slightly smaller than the major horizontal one. A crude but effective way of establishing the minimum size of the crankcase interior is by way of looking at the actual swing of the big end round the crankpin circle—all on paper. Estimate the length between the big and little end centres of the conrod and make a separate drawing of the conrod on a piece of stiff paper or light card, and cut this out to a shaped conrod blank. Stick a pin through each centre point—big end and gudgeon pin, that is—and pin it in a series of positions on the drawing with the big end centre on the crankpin circle and the gudgeon pin centre pinned on the vertical centre line. If you do this every 10 degrees or so round the crankpin circle on one side of the vertical centre line, making the outer corner points of the big end on the drawing, you can thereby plot on the drawing the actual path of the real thing, and so arrive at a crankcase size and shape that will accommodate it comfortably. Having done it on one side, the result can be copied on the other side of the vertical centre line for the complete crankcase interior.

With the space needed for the big end shown, you are now in a position to fix where the top of the crankcase must come—which is also the bottom of the cylinder barrel. Another use for the paper conrod appears at this stage, as by its use you can check that the shank of the rod will clear the bottom of the cylinder barrel in all crankshaft positions about top dead centre. When it does, then the piston can go in, which fixes the distance between the gudgeon pin and crankpin centres—hitherto an estimate. If this is much shorter than the estimate, it would be as well to check that the increased angularity of the rod does not now cause the big end to foul any part of the crankcase interior. If the final size is pretty close to your first estimate, there is unlikely to be any trouble there, unless you are cutting clearances extremely fine—and it is inadvisable to do this unless it is absolutely unavoidable.

Having drawn in the piston and the lower part of the cylinder barrel, the piston top can now be shown in top dead centre position, which fixes the length of the cylinder barrel. This can be adjusted slightly, according to the method of fixing the cylinder head and the compression ratio desired, and then the way is all clear to fill in the cylinder head.

Still considering an imaginary O.H.V. single, now would be the time to start another drawing showing the timing case, as you now know the overall dimensions of the crankcase. This could show the timing gears in outline, the cams, and the tappets. These in turn show how long the push rods will need to be, and what sort of angularity there may turn out to be on them when in position between tappets and rockers. A rough side view here would be of use, for a further check on push rod location in the other plane. If the first side view was very rough, a more careful one would be useful now, showing the crankshaft in full, checking how it works in with the bottom of the cylinder barrel, and showing shaft bearings and the depth of the timing gear. If it is a spur-driven camshaft, then some suggestion of a contact breaker would establish that this would not get in the way of anything.

A little way back I mentioned the alternative of the cylinder head as a starting point. In this case, the build-up proceeds in almost the reverse direction compared with starting with the crankshaft.

Having drawn in the cylinder head—a side view, the cylinder barrel follows next, with the top of the piston shown at top dead centre. With the depth of the piston established and the stroke known, you can now fill in the bottom edge of

11

the piston at bottom dead centre. From this you get the bottom of the cylinder barrel, and so also the top of the crankcase. A view of the big end at T.D.C. clearing the bottom end of the cylinder fixes the crankpin centre at T.D.C., and as you already know the stroke, you can now fix the point for the crankshaft centre. The con. rod, complete crankshaft and crankcase then naturally follow on as before.

On the whole, I find that in starting a set of drawings of an engine, the crankshaft is the best place to start with in the case of a single cylinder engine, but with a 4 cylinder in line engine, the cylinder head is the better jumping-off place. This is because there are questions of porting and manifolding with a multi cylinder head, and these can also be tied up with sorting out the locations of water passages from cylinder block to head and the positions of cylinder head studs. These have a bearing on the spaces between the cylinder liners in the block, which in turn govern the distances between the crankpins on the crankshaft coming immediately below the several cylinders. If you start with a four-throw crankshaft, and then find that your distances between the vertical centres of the conrods are not right for what you have to fit into the cylinder heads, then you have an awful lot of re-shuffling and re-drawing to do. It is easier to get the more complex cylinder head right first, then adjust the crankshaft to fit in with that.

With all these details completed and looking promising, then you are very nearly home and dry, and stage three drawings are looming up. I find it pays to leave things here for a day or two. Put the drawings away out of sight and leave them alone. By all means visualise them and think about odd details at times, then when you do get them out again and glance over them, it is more than likely that some little discrepancy that went unnoticed before will now stick out like the proverbial sore thumb. This is nearly your last chance to correct it! If you go ahead and make patterns for castings from your final drawings, they have got to be right, as you are then committed.

If a final careful check over after a breather shows up nothing disastrous, then the final stage three fully detailed drawing could be worked out. You may find it useful here to do separate drawings of several views of some fairly complex part or assembly—such as the cylinder head—to make absolutely sure that everything will work in all right. If everything looks fine at the completion of that stage, then you probably have something worth while that should make a viable model. It is a help sometimes to show the drawings to a knowledgeable friend, and invite him to pull the whole thing to pieces. He will probably take great delight in this! If the design stands up to his best destructive efforts, then you can feel that much more sure that it is basically sound. That is not to say that it naturally must be a successful engine! It goes no further than to confirm that it could be built; its success depends of your own knowledge of what is possible and right in an engine.

Throughout all the drawing stages there is one thing that has to be kept right in the forefront of the mind. It is of paramount importance, and it should be consciously remembered every time the smallest component sketch is completed. That one all-important thing is the question: How will I make that bit when the time comes? And "making" it is not necessarily the same thing as "machining" it. It is quite possible to work out a shape that cannot be filed true; it is all too easy to show a hole where no drill can get at it, or a tapped hole where you would have to make your own rubber tap to produce the thread! If you do come up with something of the sort, console yourself with the thought that all the best people have done it—and still do, from time to time. Look on it as a minor triumph that you spotted it before it meant scrapping some pattern work, or worse still, patterns AND castings!

There are two other points closely tied in with this question of "how will it be done?" One of these is the question of what equipment you can bring to bear, and this generally means mainly, what is the size of your lathe? If you have say, an ML7, you would probably say "Well, it is 3 ½ in. centre height, and I have a 6 in. four-jaw chuck and a 4 in. three-jaw." Yes, no doubt. But what about other essential dimensions? Can you say offhand, for instance, that you have 2 1/16 in. height available over the cross-slide, or that you can take 19/32 in. diameter down the hollow mandrel? And I swear I did not nip out into the workshop and measure those! Nor do I need to check that I can just swing 10 in. diameter in the gap, and that with either faceplate I have 1 5/8 in. available in front of it in the gap for the thickness of the job. Dimensions, clearances, and what you might call "availability statistics" like this about all your workshop equipment can be invaluable when memorised. Failing that, check them all out some time, and jot them down on one of those spare "Addresses and 'Phone Numbers" pages in your diary. Sooner or later you will run up against the question of whether to alter a component or not, the decision depending on whether you can machine it in the obvious way. If you can settle such a point straight off, by just dipping into the pocket (or memory) it makes life much more comfortable than if, to be certain, you have to go and unlock the workshop halfway down the garden and check on a cold wet night!

The other point allied to "How?" is that the casting for some component say, does not have to be exactly the shape when first cast as it will finish up. By this I mean that it can for a start incorporate a boss or lug—or more than one of either purely for the purpose of making the machining easier. It could be gripped in the chuck by the boss and almost completely machined, then the boss sawn off for the final machining of the surface on which the boss was cast—the boss making the earlier machining stages much easier to carry out. This applies particularly to thin circular items, like crankcase end covers. Where it may be desired to machine the under surface of a cylinder head, for example, the top side could well be a collection of awkward shapes quite unsuited to being gripped in the chuck, like cooling fins and/or rocker gear support pillars. A little round stub cast integral with the head in the middle of the awkward bits could be invaluable in quick and accurate setting up for machining the opposite side. Watch out that it *can* be sawn away afterwards! Note the chucking boss incorporated in the pattern for the timing case cover in the group of patterns shown in Fig. 4. After it had served its purpose as a chucking boss for facing the bolting surface of the cover, it was machined into a small housing to accommodate the crankcase breather valve, seen in the general view of the engine, Fig. 3. The same thing could apply to a small lug or "pad", placed somewhere to permit of the casting being clamped down level and firm on the cross-slide for instance, to allow of milling or fly-cutting a surface. A final machining or hand finishing stage would remove the lug to leave the desired machined shape.

This "temporary addition" technique can be applied to things other than castings. Should you want to turn a truly circular disc from something like 1/16 in. thick sheet metal, for example, it is most easily done by soft soldering it to a stub of round brass rod, and then using the stub as a chucking piece. After turning, the two pieces are warmed up to unsolder the temporary stub, which can be kept for similar use another time.

This same procedure is seen in action in a slightly different form when turning the pistons for the Mastiff engine. Here, the piston is made in two pieces silver soldered together, and the opportunity is seized to make one of the pieces much

13

longer than the piston itself requires, the extra length being used to facilitate the turning and lapping of the piston. Like a cast-on boss, the extra length is sawn off and discarded when it has served its purpose.

So this is something else worth while to bear in mind with anything of an awkward shape. Indeed, it may not only very much simplify the machining of some component, but actually make the difference between being able to retain the most suitable shape for the job and having to compromise with a less satisfactory shape, purely because of the ability to machine it.

The steps outlined in starting a design may not necessarily be your way of tackling it, but it is a way that I find works very well for me. So now, having an idea of at least one way of getting ones ideas into something like a usable form, let us have a look at individual bits and pieces and see what features make for good practice, and what things should be avoided for various reasons.

The order in which the components are looked at does not in any way indicate the order in which they should be made, but rather how they relate to others to form in some cases sub-assemblies, comprising convenient groups which could well be considered together at the design stage.

2 Crankcases, Crankshafts, Bearings, Flywheels

The building of a boat normally starts with the hull, and of a locomotive with the main frames.

The main component of the structure of a petrol engine is the crankcase, and while as its name suggests, it is a case enclosing the crank, it is normally rather more than that. The cylinder or cylinders are attached to it, and therefore it has to withstand the thrust of the pistons without deformation. In addition, it carries at least one main crankshaft bearing and generally the bearers by which the entire engine is secured to its mounting. These various functions mean that in designing an engine some thought must be given to its shape and the disposition of the metal in it, so that there is no risk of failure anywhere. These considerations rate even more important where minimum weight counts, as in an aero engine.

In model engines, crankcases are almost always of light alloy, generally in the form of castings. Single cylinder engines—particularly two-strokes—often have the crankcase and cylinder barrel combined in the one casting, which is a form of construction very suitable for engines having an overhung disc crank and a single long crankshaft bearing. The result is nicely stiff, the overall shape being one of intersecting cylinders. In this type of design, the pressures applied to the crankpin generate a "stirring" load on the shaft, tending to wring the bearing housing in a circular movement about the point of attachment to the crankcase. The usual way of combating this is to provide stiffening webs in the casting in the angle between bearing housing and crankcase end wall, and something of the sort becomes essential in a lightweight very thin crankcase.

This single bearing construction to accommodate an overhung disc crank is occasionally used in four strokes, but here the bearing cannot be so long, as timing gears, cams, tappets and associated valve gear components have to be located fairly close to the crank disc so as not to come too far out from the head. Housing these components involves a timing case, which in turn can provide an outrigger bearing for the crankshaft in the timing case cover. If this is done, some of the forces on the shaft are transmitted back to the crankcase end wall via the timing case, but as this is generally of near circular shape and has of necessity to be a fair diameter, a reasonably thin timing case wall is normally adequate.

Open ended crankcases are provided with a cover plate, which can either be a plain cover or carry additional components related to the crankshaft. Two-strokes often have a rotary admission valve mounted on the inner surface of the cover, driven by a follower engaging the crankpin. In this case the cover also carries the carburettor.

Four strokes can also have their valve gear operated in the same way, in which case the cover becomes in effect a detachable timing case. One advantage of this arrangement is that the length of the crankshaft main bearing can be increased to

15

Fig. 1. 1 c.c. O.H.V. single cylinder engine with vertically split crankcase.

two-stroke proportions, and while the length of bearings that can be accommodated in the timing case back wall and the cover plate must be much shorter, they can still be adequate for the lighter duty of operating the valve gear. One big disadvantage of this form of construction is the difficulty of assembling such an engine, where a solid big end eye is generally used, unless a very close watch is kept on component dimensions and clearances.

A natural development from this, having great advantages in ease of assembly is to combine the timing case with part of the main crankcase; in other words, to split the crankcase in a vertical plane somewhere near the middle. A further advantage of this is that a one-piece crankshaft having a bearing either side of the crank can be used, and no difficulties arise when it comes to bolting up a split big end. A vertically split crankcase naturally means that it cannot be cast in one with the cylinder barrel, and a separate bolted-on cylinder is called for. There is generally little difficulty in arranging this satisfactorily. The cylinder base flange can be square or rectangular, matching a similar top surface to the crankcase. These can both be quite small and still provide room for substantial studs and nuts in the four corners. The development of the rounded crankcase shape to the square

16

cylinder mounting surface automatically produces sufficient thickness of metal in the corner for adequate stud anchorage.

The follower-driven valve gear features can still be retained in a vertically split crankcase, with the advantage that the engine can be disassembled almost completely without losing the valve timing. A 1 c.c. O.H.V. four stroke engine incorporating these features is shown in Fig. 1. The crankcase is shown split in Fig. 2, retaining the appropriate components in each half. No attempt was made in this engine to minimise the weight, as it has a cast iron cylinder barrel machined from the solid, fabricated cast iron head, and a brass crankcase. There is no particular merit in a brass crankcase, and this material was used only because a suitable piece was available. Machining the crankcase provided an interesting exercise in boring and milling, forming the various shapes and cavities. Exactly the same procedure could be adopted with a light alloy crankcase produced from castings, which would very

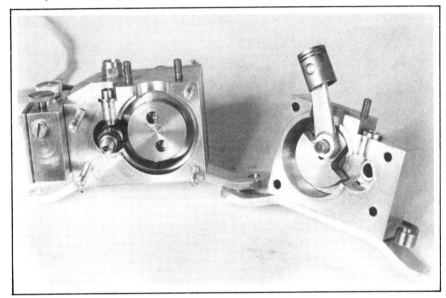

Fig. 2. Crankcase of the 1 c.c. engine split, each half retaining its internal components.

much simplify pattern making for someone who doubted his ability to cope with the more complex shapes and core-boxes required for a combined crankcase and cylinder barrel casting. This was in fact done in the case of the 3 ½ c.c. S.V. engine shown in Fig. 3, and the extremely simple patterns involved are shown in Fig. 4. This engine has a conventional brazed-up one piece crankshaft, with a split big end, the split crankcase making assembly quite straightforward.

Most of the advantages of the split crankcase are retained when the case is divided not vertically, but horizontally. The natural impulse here is to make the dividing line along the centre line of the crankshaft. An early example of a horizontally split crankcase on the crankshaft centre line is the German Benz aero engine from the 1914/18 war, now to be seen in the Shuttleworth Collection. This has separate cylinder heads held in place by long draw bolts running down into the crankcase, retaining the cylinder barrels as well. In addition, these bolts extend down through the top of the crankcase, where their lower ends serve as bolts to hold the split crankshaft bearings. For an aero engine, this is a good design point, as the crankcase with this arrangement is relieved of the power stroke stresses and

17

Fig. 3. 3½ c.c. S.V. engine, with one piece crankshaft and vertically split crankcase.

Fig. 4. The very simple patterns used for castings for the 3 ½ c.c. S.V. engine.

Fig. 5. The numerous components of a 4 c.c. 4 cylinder engine, showing the two end plates and halves of the horizontally split crankcase.

can therefore be made lighter than would otherwise be the case.

In a model, splitting the crankcase in this way can lead to snags if plain bush bearings are required. If the dividing line comes exactly across the diameter of the bearings, it is then almost impossible to fit pressed-in bearing bushes, as the tightness of the bushes in their holes—half in each part of the case—will force the halves apart sufficiently to produce severe oil leaks, if nothing worse. The same objection to a somewhat lesser extent applies to the fitting of ball bearings, where some very careful boring in the assembled crankcase is required to machine out the bearing housings to a correct fit exactly in line.

If a horizontally split crankcase has particular advantages for an individual design, there are a number of ways in which it can be retained, at the same time dodging any awkwardnesses in respect of bearings.

One way is to press fit bearing bushes into separate flanged housings, using these

19

Fig. 6. Main casting for the Westbury designed "Seal Major" engine, featuring monoblock combined cylinder block and crankcase construction.

as end cover plates for the two-piece crankcase. In this case the ends of the crank-case can be bored to a nominal diameter and the housing registers turned to a normal snug fit. As in the case of cylinder base flanges, studs in the corners of a square-flanged housing should not be too difficult to arrange satisfactorily. This type of construction can be seen in the components group Fig. 5, showing a 4 c.c. 4 cylinder O.H.V. engine before assembly. Here, cast iron crankshaft bushes are lightly pressed in and Loctited into separate crankcase end plates, which are an irregular shape to fit in with the shape of the crankcase. In this engine crankcase halves, end plates, timing case, cylinder block and cylinder head were all machined from pieces of 7/8 in. thick dural plate, but here again light alloy castings would have been equally suitable—and no doubt would have involved less machining.

Another small modification to the horizontally split crankcase to simplify bearing arrangements consists of making the split line below the bearing position. It will be apparent that if this procedure is extended as far as it can be taken, the result is an open bottom one-piece crankcase, where the bottom is closed either by a plain plate cover, or something slightly more elaborate like an oil sump. This, of course, need not be a casting like the main part of the crankcase.

When it comes to producing a model crankcase of that sort, then we have caught up with modern car engine practice. Fig. 6 shows such a casting, for the "Seal Major" engine, which also incorporates the cylinder block intended for the fitting of pressed-in cylinder liners. Pattern making for such a casting becomes quite complex, as the interior shape must be "cored out", necessitating making core boxes for the production of the appropriate moulding cores in addition to the main pattern. If you are not very experienced at this sort of work, it can pay to

20

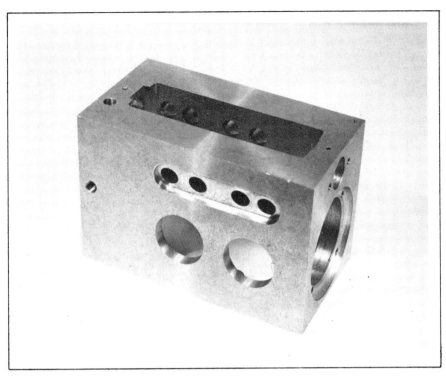

Fig. 7. The finished machined box-form crankcase for the Mastiff flat four engine.

visit the foundry you propose to patronise and make friends with the moulder. You will generally find that he will be sympathetic to the model engineer's needs, and he will probably show you some examples of small coreboxes with their cores, which will give you a good idea of what he needs to produce a usable casting.

This sort of casting is a fine example of the need to keep a strict eye on later machining procedures, when you come to work out the main features of such a component on paper.

"So," you may say, "many of the points so far mentioned would hardly seem to apply to a crankcase like that for Mastiff. What were the design points considered there?"

Well, that is a fair enough question, so let us look at it in detail—Fig. 7. For a start, the bare casting itself is an open sided box form—and that is a recognised good shape for withstanding assorted stresses. Lathe beds often take this form. When it is firmly attached to the base and has the top cover plate fitted, then it is even stiffer, as it becomes a completely closed box. The ends are very thick, providing good support for the crankshaft bearings, and their bore centres are easily located from previously machined true datum surfaces. Should it be necessary to machine the bearing housings with the casting bolted down on the cross slide, using a between centres boring bar, both bores can be machined at the same time, ensuring that they are both in line. The compact and symmetrical shape also makes for straightforward machining, without the necessity for any additional chucking pieces. The sides, while being the thinnest section present, are adequately stiff through being fairly short, and are additionally reinforced in the assembled engine by having thick and stiff plates clamped over the greater part of the outside area, the plates being the cylinder block flanges. The sides have been kept thinner than would be desirable for tapping for cylinder studs, but there is room for two out of each three studs for these to have heads on them like bolts, coming inside the case, so that they cannot pull out. The third one of each pair is tapped into the thick end, and so can be run in to a depth ample for security.

A component like a crankcase has to be not only right to withstand the various stresses generated in it, but also to stand up to additional ones imposed by other components attached to it. The Mastiff crankcase has shown itself in working conditions to be well able to do this.

So let us move on to look at the biggest component accommodated in the crankcase. Apart from the flywheel, the crankshaft in a petrol engine is also the heaviest revolving part present. It has to be well supported in suitable bearings, and so proportioned as to be able to remain stiff and undeflected against all the various forces acting on it. These will include not only the intermittent loads from the conrod, but also the centrifugal forces arising from its revolving at high speed.

The material chosen for a crankshaft depends to some extent on its shape. In a disc type crankshaft having an overhung crankpin, it might well pay to go for a steel more in the "high tensile" class than the normal mild steel. For a plain shaft of this sort where the majority of the shaping is plain turning, suitable material is likely to be more readily available in round bar form. Shafts of this sort have quite often been turned from a portion of car or lorry half-shaft, which would certainly provide all the inherent strength likely to be required. However, unless something is known of the characteristics and quality of the steel in question, it would not necessarily be superior to a more normal steel from the point of view of wear resistance. What is certain, is that it would be much tougher to machine! Some pieces of bar from such a source might in fact require annealing before they could be machined to any extent at all, and this could alter the properties considerably. In general, it is reasonable in model practice to arrange the proportions so that the shaft has adequate strength for its job when produced from normal readily available mild steel. It might be as well, to be on the safe side, to avoid the "freecutting" class of steels; these have a proportion of lead or sulphur in their make-up, and while this makes for ease of machining, it also makes for increased softness and ease of bending.

If you check the crankshaft proportions and dimensions in a modern car workshop manual, you will find that the diameters of the main journals and crankpins, in relation to the stroke of the engine, are generally surprisingly large. This is often so to the point where the big end is too wide to pass up the bore of the cylinder. The big feature aimed at here is stiffness. A moment's thought will show that any flexing or whipping of the shaft is immediately going to impose side or wringing loads on several bearings that they should not be called on to withstand. The drilling of oilways in a crankshaft from one crankpin across the web, either to another pin or to the nearest main bearing, reduces the amount of metal present in the component. This can be infinitesimal in a full size crankshaft, but considerations of carrying out deep drillings with tiny drills in a model shaft means that such drillings are often disproportionately large, compared with the full size job. This is a point to bear in mind when considering overhung crankpin disc type shafts where the crankpin is drilled for a follower pin to drive something else, like valve gear. For the follower pin to be of reasonable proportions, the crankpin will generally have to be drilled with a hole much bigger than might be needed for big

22

end lubrication, and so needs its outer diameter increased to retain sufficient strength in what amounts to a drilled shell.

In any crankshaft, where the main journals or the crankpin join the webs, there should always be a slight radius. This decreases the possibility of failure through fracture at a sharp cornered joint where there is a fair stress. In a built-up and brazed shaft, it is often convenient to let this radius be partly formed by a fillet of the brazing spelter or silver solder. When making such a shaft by brazing together several components, it is always sound practice to make the several pieces slightly larger than finished size, and then to machine them as if the whole were a casting. This ensures getting the various diameters exactly right, with their surfaces of clean metal free from scale from the heating. It does provide the ability too, to be able to "machine out" any slight distortion that may have been caused by the brazing. In the machining of a built-up shaft, leaving the small radius at the ends of journals and pins is quite likely to leave a thin ring of brazing spelter showing round the radius. This will do no harm, as it cannot take any appreciable load, even when running against similar bronze type bearing metal.

Crankshaft main bearing journals should be reasonably proportioned, and a safe working rule here is to make them at least as long as their diameter—preferably more. This is so that the oil film in the bearing, however supplied, is not readily squeezed out from each end. Remember that if the oil is supplied via a drilled hole in the middle of a bearing bush, then the oil has less than half the width of the bearing to travel before it is escaping at the side of the bearing. This, of course, will not apply where ball races are fitted. A scale drawing of a car engine will show that the big end bearings do not seem to conform to such proportions, but here it must be remembered that the oil supply is at much greater pressure than would ever be used in a model engine—if, indeed it is supplied under pressure at all—and in much more copious supply.

The proportions of a model multi generally seem automatically to provide reasonable room for big end bearings of adequate width, and where possible, this should certainly be taken advantage of up to nearly enough the "equal proportions" shape.

The whole question of lubrication covers quite a number of points, so we might consider some of the main ones in a separate chapter when we can look at the crankshaft as one of the main components concerned.

There have been model engines built in which a built-up crankshaft has been employed, but not a one-piece shaft; that is, the shaft is composed of two or more parts assembled in such a way that the shaft can be taken apart again if required. These have generally been engines closely following motor cycle practice, where the shaft has been either a pair of flywheels with integral short main shafts assembled with a separate crankpin, or else the equivalent of an overhung disc crank with the addition of another disc with integral shaft attached to the crankpin. The advantages of this type of construction are that a one piece ring type of big end can be used, which eliminates any possible weaknesses resulting from using a bolted up split big end; a ball or roller big end can be fitted, and the flywheel(s) come close to the actual crank and are well supported by the main bearings.

The disadvantages are that a much larger crankcase is generally needed to house the flywheels, if they are to be big enough to serve a useful function, and the major one—some very nice precision machining is called for to produce a rigid shaft that is really true in all respects.

One highly desirable feature in any crankshaft, be it single or multi, is that the bearings should support the shaft as closely as possible to the crankpin. For one thing, in a multi crankshaft, this reduces the "couple" effect. What is a couple? Well, it is easier to invite you to see its effect for yourself than to explain it.

If you do not happen to own a bicycle, then drop in on a friend who does, and borrow his (or hers!) for a minute and try this experiment. Stand the cycle upside down on its saddle and handlebars. Then grasping the nearest pedal, give it a hearty spin backwards, so that the pedals and driving chainwheel freewheel. While the pedals and chainwheel are spinning, they will transmit quite a strong wriggling and squirming motion to the whole cycle, so that you may have to hold it quite firmly to prevent it falling over. The effect dies out as the speed of the pedals drops, naturally. That wriggling motion is the visible effect of the couple formed by the two pedals—two unbalanced masses revolving 180 deg. apart, and not in the same plane. In the case of a multi-cylinder crankshaft, any two cranks 180 deg. apart will form a couple, and the design of the crankshaft should conteract this effect as far as possible. In the normal four cylinder car engine, Nos. 1 and 2 cranks will form a couple, as will 3 and 4. However, Nos. 2 and 3 both come the same side of the shaft, so that the couple that Nos. 1 and 2 form is anti-phase to that of 3 and 4, and so the two couples act against each other, as nearly as possible cancelling out.

The Mastiff engine is not quite the same as a four cylinder in line in this respect, it being a four cylinder opposed. Nevertheless, the crankshaft is much the same, as the two middle crankpins both come the same side of the shaft. Unlike the four-in line, the two cylinders acting on the two middle pins are horizontally opposed, but if you take a look at the conrod order of assembly on the shaft you will see that any couple produced by the first two cylinders is still in opposition to that from the last two.

This is one angle to the whole question of balance, and this is a big enough subject to merit a chapter to itself. There is just one other thing that might be noted at this point, and that is that to keep the best possible balance and avoid odd couples as far as possible, in any model multi a lot can be done with the proportions on the crankshaft itself to further this end. If you check over the dimensions of the Mastiff crankshaft, you will find that there are exactly equal sizes of crank webs each side of the shaft centre line; while the end crankpins are of a different length to the centre double one, the centre one is exactly twice the length of either of the two short end ones. The basic proportions of the shaft ensure that it should be at least in static balance, and it is probably not far off dynamically, either.

There is a difference between static and dynamic balance. If you take a simple bar, drilled in the middle so that it can revolve on a pin, and add a weight of 4 ozs. 1 in. from the middle hole, and then at the other end add a weight of 1 oz. 4 ins. away from the hole, the beam will balance when placed on the pin. Thus it is statically balanced; it balances when not in motion. If you spin the bar vigorously on its pin, it will show by the forces tending to make the pin swing in a circle, that it is not perfectly balanced when spinning. That is, it is not dynamically balanced— balanced when in motion. This is because the centrifugal forces acting on the two weights have differing effects, because of the different distances of the weights from the bearing point. This, applied to a model crankshaft, means that the shaft must be symmetrical both as to the disposition of the various masses of metal, and as to their location about the shaft centre line.

Any out of balance forces generated by the crankshaft show up as vibrations of

24

the whole engine—probably worse at one or more particular speeds. On some high-speed two-strokes, any such vibrations at low and medium speeds are largely ignored, as they seem to diappear at high speeds. They are, in fact, still there, and building up at higher speeds to contribute still greater stresses, but due to their very high speed, the intertia of the main mass of the engine prevents the engine moving as a whole to show their existence, so they merely add unwanted loads to the revolving components.

And talking of revolving components, mounted on the crankshaft is the biggest of the lot—the flywheel. A first impression might well be that there is little to be said about flywheels, but they deserve a little thought all the same.

The main consideration is of course weight, and weight in the right place. The most normally used material is either cast iron or steel. If absolute maximum weight in a small bulk is a prime consideration, then bronze is slightly better, but its cost these days generally swings the balance in favour of one of the other two. An iron casting is generally perfectly satisfactory, although there is always the very slight chance that the casting might contain a small blowhole or gas bubble in some part of the thicker section, which is not revealed in machining. Should this be the case, then the wheel will not be balanced after machining. The way to check this is to make up a dummy crankshaft end, duplicating the way the flywheel is to be attached to the shaft, and extending the ends of the dummy shaft so that it can be poised on knife edges and gently rolled along. Any tendency for the wheel to come to rest with the same point lowest every time will soon show up, and then the presence of something like a blowhole can be suspected. It is a comparatively simple matter to correct this, by drilling a shallow dimple in some inconspicuous place near the edge of the rim—probably in the back face. Any corrective measures of this sort need to be carried out very gingerly, a very little at a time, as this sort of test is quite sensitive and the amount of unbalance may be very small. If you do overdo it, then you will have to re-correct with another smaller dimple on what was originally the lighter side.

Flywheels machined from the solid, in either mild steel or bronze, will not be likely to suffer from this, and it can be taken for granted that if the whole of the surfaces are machined and the wheel runs truly as a whole, then it is in balance. Small brass flywheels, which would generally be produced from castings, might well be tried out for balance, especially if they are inteded for use on a high speed engine. Any evidence of unbalance would naturally be dealt with in the same way.

Spoked flywheels are very unlikely to be fitted permanently to small petrol engines, being normally confined to the larger stationary type gas or oil engines, following the fashion of the prototype. If, in machining a spoked flywheel, a cleaning up cut is taken round the inner edge of the rim just where the spokes blend in, and some careful filing of the spokes carried out to get these nicely identical, the balance should be fair enough. It could well show some slight unbalance through minute differences in spoke thickness or radius at the roots, but in view of the slow speed of the type of engine it would be intended for, this could safely be ignored. Only do please make sure that any unbalance is not due to a wobbly or eccentric flywheel; on a slow revving engine, nothing looks worse! One of the pleasures in watching a traction engine ticking over is the way that big flywheel turns leisurely over, running dead true. You can sometimes spot a shade of run-out on the rim, but it is generally pretty minute. In industry, the presence of a blow-hole, its exact location and its size could be spotted by the use of X-rays, but this is hardly a technique that the model engineer could apply—even if it were worth it.

One of the things to aim at in deciding the size of an engine flywheel is to make it of as large a diameter as possible, but at the same time as light as will serve to promote smooth running of the engine. The outside diameter is generally governed by the intended use of the engine, or by its method of mounting. In an engine intended for a boat, for instance, the diameter must be kept down to a size where no point on the rim extends further from the crankshaft centre line than the lowest point of the engine crankcase. This is so that the engine can be mounted in the boat as low as possible to line up with the propeller shaft. In any sort of stationary engine, this is nothing like so important, and it is quite usual to see some part of large flywheel rims sunk into a recess in the floor or engine mounting. Flywheels treated in this way are often spoked wheels, and the thought may occur, if a spoked wheel is of such a diameter that it has to be partly accommodated in a pit, would it not be preferable to make it a heavier, solid wheel that could be mounted to clear the normal floor level?

There are several reasons combining to make it preferable to use the spoked wheel. For one thing, if it is a really big fellow, then the spoked wheel is easier handled for mounting and removing from the crankshaft, as lifting tackle can be easily rigged to lift it by the rim. Being lighter than the smaller solid one would be, there is less load on the crankshaft bearings and the shaft itself, which is always a worth while point. Then, probably the biggest point, the effectiveness of a flywheel is increased considerably if the diameter can be increased, as the main weight—that in the rim—is operating at a greater radius from the shaft centre. Or looked at from the other way, if you can increase the diameter of the wheel, then you can get the same flywheel effect with a lighter wheel. Take a look at some of the very slender, but large diameter flywheels normally fitted to the old steam beam engines, and you will see this effect very well illustrated. Don't forget too, that these old engines ran at a very slow speed, so that really effective flywheel action was essential.

To come down to basics, the function of a flywheel is to absorb and give out energy—to absorb it when the engine is producing power, and to give it back when it is not. The flywheel's ability to do this depends on three things; its mass, its speed and its size. By varying any one of these factors, so you alter the amount of energy the wheel can handle. A textbook on mechanics will give you all the mathematical proofs and data necessary to calculate these values, but skipping the maths in detail, it can be said that if you double all the dimensions of a flywheel, its effectiveness as a flywheel goes up by the fifth power, i.e., by 32 times. This doubling up all round will cube its weight, i.e., will multiply it by 8. So it will be obvious that increasing the dimensions of a flywheel will increase its effectiveness by very much more than the straight proportion. This feature can be taken advantage of in another way; in the case of a plain disc flywheel, if you double the diameter but keep the weight the same, the effectiveness as a flywheel goes up by a factor of sixteen times.

If the speed of the flywheel is increased, then the effectiveness again goes up, and this in practice generally means that a really high speed engine can do with a smaller (or lighter) flywheel than can a much slower speed engine. This is very noticeable in respect of car engine flywheels. The really old vintage car engines generally had a massive external flywheel. Such a wheel absorbed considerable power to accelerate it. With the gradual development of engines of much higher speed and the need for considerably greater acceleration, a much slimmer and lighter flywheel was used which absorbed less power in acceleration, but was still sufficient at the higher speed at which it was run. This has reached the point for purely high speed sprint cars, where it is no uncommon thing to find light aluminium alloy flywheels fitted. In model engines of course, there is generally little need for especially good acceleration to be evident, so that the engine's normal speed range would be the main factor.

These are points to bear in mind when fixing the size of the flywheel for a new engine, and it is reasonable practice to specify the largest flywheel that can comfortably be fitted, keeping the weight down to the minimum necessary for efficient running. As the weight becomes more effective the further it is located from the shaft centre, it stands to reason that the hub and parts of the wheel close in to the centre contribute little to the general flywheel effect. This means that in the case of a solid flywheel, the disc part of the wheel between hub and rim need be little more than a thin connecting web, serving only to mount the heavy rim on the hub. In a small diameter solid wheel, by the time the hub has been left big enough in machining to accept the mounting arrangment on the shaft and a fair thickness of rim provided, there may be little more than a wide groove to be machined in the face to produce the thin web. This is still worth doing nevertheless, if only to reduce the weight of that part of the wheel having little effect, to reduce general wear.

As the whole of the power absorbed by the flywheel and transmitted back to the engine is via its attachment to the crankshaft, this obviously needs to be amply secure. There are various acceptable methods of securing flywheels, some more suited to one type of engine than another. In the case of very slow speed engines, the flywheel is very often secured on a parallel portion of the crankshaft by a parallel or wedge shaped key, seated either in a keyway in the shaft or merely a flat on it. This is not really good enough for a much faster running petrol engine, where the higher speeds, vibration—and in all cases except stationary engines, movement of the engine itself—can very well induce movement of the flywheel along its seat on the shaft. A keyed wheel is quite frequently used here, but with the possible end movement of the wheel along the shaft controlled by seating the wheel tightly on a taper or arranging for it to be clamped against a shoulder on the shaft, in both cases by a nut on the shaft holding it secure. A very positive fixing results from the use of splines, but these are very rarely found in model petrol engines where much simpler devices can be used just as effectively.

There is much to be said for the use of a taper fitting, which ensures that the flywheel is pulled up positively on its seating to run truly every time. However, keying the wheel on the taper can, in some circumstances, be a little too positive. If the taper fitting takes the form of a taper collet on a parallel shaft, then the disadvantages of a key are eliminated. The collet fitting, while it can be assembled tightly enough to be perfectly satisfactory, can be made to slip under extreme conditions of load. A fast revving boat engine for instance, should it accidentally take a long cold drink of pond water, will stop very smartly indeed—generally to the extent of doing considerable internal damage to the engine. This can be minimised a bit if the flywheel is fixed to the shaft by a collet, as this will slip a little momentarily and limit the twisting forces on the shaft. Depending on the sturdiness of the shaft, this could make the difference between salvaging the shaft and having to make a new one.

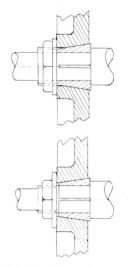

Fig. 8. Alternative types of flywheel collet.

The collet fixing can take two forms—Fig. 8 one being a plain collet butting against a shoulder on the shaft, a nut on the shaft pressing the wheel on the collet to compress it. Where for any reason it is desired to keep the shaft plain and with no part threaded for the nut, then the collet can incorporate its own threaded

27

sleeve for the flywheel nut. This type, as compared with the plain collet, can have two slight disadvantages. The collet itself must be slightly larger in diameter, as its smaller end must be big enough to provide for the screwed sleeve part. This in turn means that the flywheel boss must be that much bigger to accept the fatter collet, and this may not always be acceptable. The other point is that the nut must be pulled up tight with a modicum of restraint, or there is a distinct risk of wringing the screwed portion off the collet. When the collet and the matching taper in the flywheel are carefully and accurately machined, both types are very effective, and either can be used with confidence in any engine to which the appearance is appropriate. Just for the record, all my engines and several of E.T. Westbury's use the palin collet and threaded shaft fixing. A suitable angle for all the taper fittings mentioned is about 10 degrees included angle.

When a flywheel has been secured on a closely fitting collet—especially if it has been in position for some time—it will be wedged very securely on the taper. When it comes to removing it, unless some provision has been made for pulling it neatly, its removal can be something of a problem. The easiest way of simplifying this is to drill the web of the wheel in two opposite places and tap the holes. 2 BA is quite big enough for most types of flywheels likely to need this treatment. To draw the wheel, all you need then is a short stout bar drilled 2 BA clearing to match the hole spacing in the wheel, and two lengths of studding. The bar goes across the end of the shaft, with the studs passing through the holes and into the holes in the wheel. Nuts on the studs outside the bar are pulled up half a turn at a time alternately, till the wheel is pulled loose. Sometimes the wheel goes hard all the way, as the collet slips stiffly along the shaft rather than the collet letting go in the taper of the wheel hub. If the collet is still tight in the wheel hub when it is completely removed a light tap with a piece of rod in the small end of the tapered wheel bore will jar it free.

As most model petrol engines are started with a cord looped round a pulley on the crankshaft, provision is often made for this by turning the cord groove in the flywheel rim. The larger the flywheel, the slower the starting speed, and this state of affairs can be improved on by providing a smaller starting pulley in one with the flywheel. This again, is often seen. While it is much less frequently featured, it is quite easy to fit a separate starting pulley to the face of the flywheel; if a couple of wheel-pulling tapped holes are provided in the flywheel, these can be used as a ready-made means of attaching a starting pulley. This way was adopted for Mastiff, so that the pulley could be omitted if starting with a front end starting dog was preferred, without altering the construction in any way.

As it would seem that flywheels are closely tied up with starting—for models at least—we could treat the two things together and have a look at some points about starting.

In working out a design for a new engine, it pays handsomely to make sure that the starting arrangements are adequate while still at the "on paper" stage. If these should be overlooked, and have to be worked in when the engine is under construction, afterthought additions nearly always tend to be something of a make-shift, and therefore that much less effective than something properly designed and incorporated from the start.

Starting arrangements normally take two forms; either some version of the cord already mentioned, or a starting dog on the nose of the crankshaft as in a car engine or small industrial engines for hand starting. A crankshaft dog is quite straightforward to make, and as is quite often done, can be made to stand in as a timing pinion retaining nut. Some older engines featured the starting dog on the protruding end of the camshaft, the idea being that you obtained a faster cranking speed on the crankshaft through the 2 : 1 timing gears. This is not an awfully good idea really, as it puts a considerable strain on the gears and in particular on any keys used to locate them. With this system you could too, find yourself obliged to operate the starting left-handed, owing to the reversal of direction through the timing gears. This tends to be a rather awkward movement.

The short length of shaft engaging the dog can be used direct by means of a T-handle held in the hand, or in a hand drill for the sake of the faster cranking speed and the continuous turning possible. For the sake of a really fast and continuous starting speed with the minimum of effort, it is not unknown for an electric drill to be used!

The business end of the starting shaft engaging the crankshaft dog generally takes the form of a cross pin to engage the notches of the dog, with probably a round end to the shaft, like a car starting handle. In use, this is prone to be flung out of engagement in a sideways direction when the engine fires. The way may be clear for this to happen without risk of damage anywhere, but the design may well feature some part of the engine which could suffer if repeatedly knocked with the shaft. This is the case with Mastiff, where the distributor comes quite close to the starting dog on the crankshaft, and as the distributor is of Paxolin, it is obviously somewhat vulnerable. A form of starter was therefore worked out which obviates this danger, and also gives a much more controlled sort of action. The construction of this is described in "Model Engineer" of 20th September 1974.

Re-coil starters are frequently found on lawn mower and outboard boat engines. Here, the starting cord is a single length wound round a drum, fixed at its inner end. When the cord has been pulled out smartly to spin the engine, on relaxing the pull on the cord a spring in the drum re-winds the cord ready for another pull. These have occasionally been fitted to model engines, when they have taken the form of a separate unit fitted in line with the engine crankshaft. There would appear to be no "standard" form of re-coil starter for model engines, and those that have been made have been tailored for the individual engine. There is generally some experimental work involved, in balancing length of cord, length and strength of re-coil spring, suitable mounting, and all the other requirements that a particular engine calls for. A more or less universal starter of this type would be extremely useful— if anyone cared to devote some time and effort to working out a suitable design!

In the course of talking about crankcases and crankshafts, bearings have been referred to a number of times, so this might be a convenient point at which to take a look at these.

There have been lots of textbooks on the subject of bearings (M.A.P. publish a useful one) and any of these will give you useful information on the subject. The main thing is to choose a bearing material compatible with the material of the shaft running in it. The bearings met with in model engines will for the most part be plain bushes or sleeve bearings, and will probably be machined from stock rod.

Crankshaft and conrod bearings in car engines are usually of softish special alloy. This is because the loading on these bearings much more resembles a "shock load" than does the load on say, a more leisurely running steam engine. The bearing metal used in the car engine is therefore less liable to failure than some harder and more brittle material, through providing something of a cushioning effect. Modern manufacturing methods now produce these bearings in the form of a thin skin cast on to the surface of a shell made from stiffer metal, but this way of making bearings is unlikely to be met with or used in model engines.

The main crankshaft bearings will generally be flanged bushes, and one of the bronzes is generally specified for these. I personally prefer gunmetal—another member of the same family. The advantage of this is that it is rather more easily machined, and being less "clingy" it is more easily drilled and reamed. If a bearing bush is being bored out in the lathe, a keen, slightly round nosed tool used at a low to moderate speed will produce a mirror finish. This material seems to work very well with the quality mild steel that would be used for a crankshaft.

A useful design point here that it could pay to bear in mind is that the engine castings will probably all be of light alloy. Most non-ferrous foundries producing light alloy castings also handle gunmetal. If the engine components include one or two gunmetal items, plus say, a couple of biggish main bearing bushes, it is good practice to make one of the patterns for a gunmetal casting to include a cylinder of metal big enough to provide enough material for the bearings. This not only enables you to get away with one pattern for three items, but saves the moulder time and effort—and so saves you money! He only has to cast one item, when a simple sawing job on the casting gives you the basic component plus two bushes. This was done in the case of the Mastiff oil pump casting (the only gunmetal item), where the sleeve for the drive shaft was extended to include the two main bearing bushes Fig. 9.

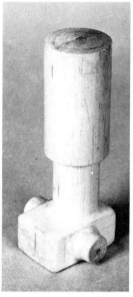

Fig. 9. Pattern for an oil pump body to be cast in gunmetal. The enlarged cylinder at the top provides material for the engine's main bearing bushes.

Mention was made, when talking of mounting bearing bushes in crankcases, of pressing them into detachable end plates. If this is done, the bush should have a reasonable wall thickness, otherwise the tightness of the press fit will compress the bush slightly, making it much too tight about the shaft running in it. It is quite easy to run into the state of affairs where the bush requires another pass through of the reamer to restore the former nice fit on the shaft, yet it is not held tightly enough in its mounting plate to resist the twist of the reamer. A heavy press fit is not advisable anyway, because of the risk of splitting the bearing housing in the light alloy plate. The best course to avoid all these awkwardnesses is to make the outer diameter of the bush a snug slip fit in its housing, and then seal it in position with Loctite. This will give a dependably secure fixture in the simplest possible way, with no possibility of distortion of either bush or housing. This technique can be used with bushes of any material.

One material with outstanding wear characteristics is cast iron. This gives its best results with a hardened and polished shaft, but does work reasonably well with a mild steel shaft if the journals are finished as good as you can possibly get them. The baby 4 c.c. 4 cylinder engine has thin cast iron main bearing bushes secured in place by Loctite, and these seem to be quite satisfactory so far in conjunction with the mild steel crankshaft.

Where ball bearings are involved, there are one or two points to bear in mind for the best results. The bearing can be lightly pressed into the housing with less risk of distrotion than with a thin-walled bush, as the outer race is of hardened steel and very stiff. The fit of the shaft in this inner race needs to be a stiff push fit if not otherwise held, to ensure that the rotary movement is taken in the bearing and not by the shaft running round in the inner member. If the shaft is supported by a bearing at each end, provision should be made for slight lengthwise movement of the shaft, such as is most likely to arise from it warming up. This provision is normally at one end only, and it must be decided at the "on paper" stage which end bearing it is best to locate positively. In the case of a crankshaft, this is most satisfactorily arranged to come at the timing end. At the fixed end, the inner race

30

can be clamped by a nut against a shoulder on the shaft, or nipped by a timing gear, spacer collar or other component on the shaft. If the outer race is not pressed into its housing, it can be clamped by a cover plate or ring, taking care that this clears the inner race edge and any ball cage that the bearing make have. At the "floating" end, the shaft is normally the component where any movement is arranged to occur, a tightish push fit in the bearing being relied on to ensure that the bearing spins properly. If the possible movement is provided for at the shaft, then the outer race can be pressed into its housing similar to the opposite end. Note that the fixed end bearing housing should be readily detachable, so that the shaft can be removed, leaving the bearing properly fitted.

Like plain bearing bushes, ball races can be Loctited into their housings, with the same resulting advantages. Should this be done, the outer surface of the bearing should be given a slight rub round with fine sandpaper, just to produce a slight scratching of the highly polished surface. This very considerably helps the Loctite to get a more secure hold than it could on the perfectly smooth unmarked surface. Needless to say, every possible care should be taken to see that no smallest particle of abrasive gets into the race itself.

The original idea of ball bearings was that they should run dry, as the movement is rolling rather than sliding. In practice, they never are run dry, but need no sort of special liquid oil supply such as a plain bearing could use. However, a supply of oil should be catered for, and it is quite sufficient to ensure that the bearing is exposed to oil mist.

As a final point it should be noted that if there be any end thrust involved in a shaft running in ball bearings, it is most important to choose a type of bearing that is designed to accept this.

One other type of bearing that it might pay to bear in mind at the design stage is the porous sintered bronze bush. These are available commercially in a wide range of sizes, and are fabricated in such a way as to produce a fine-grain porous bearing material. These are initially soaked in oil which provides lubrication for a considerable time. It is a common sense move to ensure that some oil gets trapped in a small well with a hole drilled at the bottom to communicate with a point on the outside of the bush in order to keep the bush well soaked, but the bush itself should not be drilled for a direct oil feed like a plain bronze or gunmetal bush. These Oilite bushes can be pressed into position reasonably tightly, as their dimensions are arranged to allow for the probable amount of compression resulting from pressing in. This type of bush is likely to be more satisfactory in a lightly loaded bearing, such as a contact breaker drive shaft or similar, rather than a high speed heavily loaded bearing like a main crankshaft bearing subject to fluctuating loads.

3 Cylinders, Cylinder Heads

Although a petrol engine cylinder (excluding the head) is a straightforward item, there are several variations of construction on which to ring the changes in order to produce the most suitable version for an intended engine.

Unquestionably the most suitable material is cast iron—although not necessarily for the whole cylinder. The essential requirements of the material are that it should be readily machinable to a parallel bore with a good internal finish, and that it should have good wearing properties. Cast iron is excellent on all these points, having also the characteristic that in use it develops a very useful low-friction glaze on the working surface. One commercially produced two-stroke employs a hard brass liner chrome plated in the bore. A hard chrome surface has good wearing properties where lubrication is efficient at all times, but any lubrication failure, or accidental introduction of abrasive "foreign matter" might have a more damaging effect on such a surface than on the more conventional cast iron.

Given that a cast iron cylinder bore is thoroughly good practice, one way—and the original way—of producing this is to make the entire barrel of cast iron. For an air-cooled engine where weight is not of primary importance, this is still a good way and the cylinders of the engine shown in Figs. 1 and 3 were both machined from the solid. Ground centrifugally cast iron stick is available in a range of diameters, which makes the machining a straightforward procedure. An iron casting can be used, and frequently is, which much reduces the amount of metal to be removed from the bore, but with a casting there is always some slight risk of running into a hard spot or small blow-hole in the boring. A hard spot can be big enough to take the edge off the boring tool, or small enough to pass un-noticed until you find that if has deflected the tool slightly just at the one spot, with the result that the bore is not parallel throughout. There is no guarantee that this can successfully be lapped out, although if all the other machining is complete it is always worth trying. A blow-hole in the bore generally means replacing the casting and starting again.

For a cast iron bore in a cylinder of some other material, this means an iron sleeve housed in the cylinder proper. This could be to save weight in an air-cooled cylinder, or to provide a cast iron bore in a light alloy water cooled cylinder.

In the case of a light alloy cylinder with inserted liner, the machining involves two accurate bores, as it is highly desirable that the sleeve should make close contact with the bore of the jacket over its whole area. This, of course, is so that the cooling sleeve can conduct the heat away from the hot liner as effectively as possible. As good a way as any of achieving this is by way of a "shrink fit", in which the jacket is bored to an interference fit and then heated, to be slipped hot over the cold sleeve. On cooling it contracts, to grip immovably on the liner. In small size cylinders, the actual amount of expansion is very small indeed, so that some experimenting might be advisable to establish the best interference dimensions. It would be as well too, in any such trials, to standardise the different temperatures of the sleeve and jacket by say, immersing the jacket in boiling water and leaving the sleeve in a refrigerator for a set time.

Incidentally, for those unfamiliar with the term "interference fit", this signifies the type of fit of two components, one to be inserted in the bore of the other, where the bore is actually very minutely smaller than the outside diameter of the component to be inserted. Assembly is therefore carried out by forcing the one into the other, in the case of model size components generally by using the vice, or a long draw-bolt through both, the pressure being applied by a nut being screwed down the bolt, the bolt head and nut bearing on drilled plates each end. Components assembled with an interference fit are generally fitted cold via pressure; the term shrink fit indicates that the one item is heated and the other kept cold, so that the size difference is just about cancelled out, and the two can be fitted together without the need for heavy pressure. When both revert to normal temperature, the fit is just as tight as in the case of the force-fitted pair without the heat difference. Tables can be referred to, showing the heaviness of the fit, depending on the material of the components and their size, giving the actual dimensional difference between the bore of the one and the outside diameter of the other. Like many other tables referring to full size practice, these are of doubtful value in the case of model engineering sizes.

Where an iron liner is inserted tightly in a light alloy cylinder, there is in theory at least, some danger of the cylinder jacket becoming loose in running, owing to the greater expansion of the jacket as compared with the iron liner. In practice, I have never had this happen, nor known anyone else who has. This may be partly due to the fact that the expansion difference is to some extent cancelled out, as the liner will always be somewhat hotter than the jacket.

There are other ways in which a secure fit can be obtained. In the Westbury designed "Ensign" engine, the light alloy cylinder jacket was cast direct round a steel sleeve placed in the casting mould, so that the molten metal could set around the sleeve for a permanent joint. The other way of obtaining a firm mechanical fixing is to make the sleeve a slip fit in the jacket and secure it in position by the use of Loctite. This is perhaps the easiest practical way mechanically, although the different expansion rate objection applies here too. There is also an additional factor; the bond obtained from the use of Loctite is a plastic film, and this is an insulator. Hence the heat transference from line to jacket might not be quite so good as with a metal-to-metal joint. Another point is that there is a temperature limit above which a Loctited joint will let go, although this is high enough to be well above the temperature which a model petrol engine would normally attain. However, like many other procedures to which there are objections, even with a high performance air-cooled engine—it works! In the case of a Loctite secured liner in a water-cooled cylinder block, the temperatures would be considerably less, and therefore the risks mentioned that much more remote.

The question of working temperature is naturally linked to that of cooling the cylinder. An air-cooled cylinder is normally provided with fins on the outside to increase the area of metal exposed to the cooling air, and depending on the construction of the cylinder, these may be either cast or machined in. Fins on a sand casting cannot be moulded cleanly as thin or as closely spaced as ones machined in. The ability to machine very thin, closely spaced fins is sometimes carried to excess, so that the idea of the fins is largely defeated through their being too close to each other to allow free accesss to their roots by the cooling air. The source of the heat

33

is at the roots, where the cooling is needed most. The section of the fin should ideally be tapered, with a radius each side where the fins join the barrel. While I have never seen any ideal proportions for cooling fins laid down, it is probably true that this is one of those things where, if in the light of experience it looks right then it probably is so. Reasonable fin proportions would result from regarding say 25% of the bore dimension as the maximum depth, maximum root thickness equal to about 3/8 of fin depth, and spaced at not less than twice root thickness apart. An authoritative work on full size petrol engines, in giving the details of an air-cooled engine on which numerous tests and trials were carried out, mentions in passing that the fins were .35 D, ("D" being the bore diameter), their pitch was .10 D, and their root radius was .018 D.

In a small air-cooled light alloy cylinder jacket intended to be cast from the simplest possible pattern, from all points of view it could pay to have the fin area cast solid and machine in the fins for the sake of neatness and regular slim proportions.

One other point with regard to temperature and air-cooled cylinders: that is, it is almost impossible to have the cylinder base flange too thick. Most of the components which get hot in a petrol engine dissipate a fair part of their heat through conduction into other components in contact with them. The piston loses most of its heat through contact with the cylinder walls; valves through their contact with seatings and guides; liners through their jackets. The cylinder head—especially an O.H.V. job—passes heat on to the cylinder barrel. And the cylinder itself? Obviously a significant proportion of its heat passes into the crankcase, and this is through its base flange bolted tightly to the top of the crankcase. This transfer will take place to an even greater extent when the cylinder barrel and crankcase are both parts of the one casting.

So the heat transfer is assisted by having the cylinder flange massive enough to provide a fair amount of metal for the easiest heat flow. There are also two further points, both of which call for a fairly hefty flange. One is that this flange will take all the kicks from the piston, and these are shear and bending stresses on the corners of the flange. Both cast iron and light alloy resist compression strains better than those in other directions. The other point is that should you want to increase the compression ratio very slightly, the base of the flange is a convenient place from which to skim off a trifle to lower the cylinder head down closer to the piston crown. That is, of course, provided you have enough thickness there in the first place for this to be a safe operation! A point to watch carefully, should you do this, is to make sure that the bottom edge of the cylinder barrel is not lowered enough to either foul the crankshaft or the conrod.

Water cooled cylinders mostly rely on inserted liners in models, and these can be either "wet" or "dry"—the difference being that the wet liner has the water in direct contact with the outer surface of the liner, while the dry type is housed in a full length machined bore, with the water circulating on the outside of the bored shell housing the liner. In the dry type, the same considerations will apply to the fitting as affect the liner in an air-cooled jacket. In the wet type, the area of jacket in contact with the liner is much less and is confined to two belts—above and below the water space—so that good fits are essential where liner and jacket come into contact. Note that in this case, the upper and lower contact belts need not be the same size. Where the liner is inserted from the top, the job of seating it in position can be eased somewhat by making the lower bore and liner diameter slightly less than those at the top, then the liner will drop in freely for most of the way, requiring to be pressed in only for a distance equal to the depth of the bored jacket rings.

The fitting can be made easier still in some circumstances by making the bottom fit a hand push fit, and sealing the joint watertight by means of a rubber ring trapped and compressed between a small shoulder turned on the bottom of the liner and the bottom of the water space where the liner enters the bore. The depth of the space occupied by the ring is arranged in the machining so that the ring is compressed sufficiently when pressing home the liner to make a completely watertight joint. Thus there is only one press fit between liner and jacket—that at the top. Note that the liner diameter in this case must be considerably larger at the top than at the bottom, so that the large diameter contacting the ring can pass freely through the top bore in the jacket. This necessity makes this method unacceptable for some engines, where space is at a premium. It can often be used with benefit however, in the case of horizontal gas or oil engine models.

When designing an engine employing wet liners, it should be borne in mind that the top of the water space should not come too near the top of the cylinder, even if it appears to be curtailing the depth of the water space somewhat. If the water space extends too high, it will have the effect of reducing the contact area of the top belt—which in some cases could be a gas pressure joint—and so decreasing the certainty of a watertight joint. What is equally undesirable is that it could also have the effect of reducing the depth of metal at the top of the jacket to a thickness insufficient for a secure anchorage for the cylinder head studs.

A further design point in this connection is that it is good policy to try and locate as many cylinder head studs as possible to screw into solid metal outside the water space, so ensuring that their holes can be tapped amply deep for a secure hold. In Mastiff, this has been attained for all the studs except one near each cylinder.

When it comes to cylinder heads, starting with the S.V. version, these are generally much less complex from all points of view than those for O.H.V. engines. Like the other main components of the engine, they generally take the form of light alloy castings, with the minimum of machining being necessary. Cooling fins can quite well be cast in the majority of cases, as the machining of these from the solid would be much more complicated than is the turning in of fins round a symmetrical cylinder barrel. The pattern for an air-cooled S.V. head is quite straightforward to make, the fins being thin tapered plywood strips let into slots cut in the shaped block for the body of the head. Pads for the cylinder head nuts to bear on are just short stubs of round dowel rod glued into shallow holes in the top of the pattern, being flattened where necessary to allow them to fit between pairs of fins where their location makes this necessary. A typical example is shown in the group of patterns, Fig. 4.

With the majority of conventionally shaped S.V. heads it is preferable to have the underside cast quite flat, and to machine out the internal shape of the combustion space by end-milling. Home-made slot drills can cope with this quite satisfactorily. The recess to be machined out is in most cases quite shallow, so that there is little metal to be machined away. Little is to be gained by having this cavity cast in; if it is cast in, the surface will probably be rough enough from the mould to require some finishing off—a little awkward to carry out by hand methods. If however, the shape is machined out, the finish from the tool is quite good enough to require no further attention. Furthermore, if a flat surface is first faced in the lathe, then you have an extremely good surface on which to mark out boundary lines and centres for the subsequent machining of the recess. This also eliminates any possibility of a cast-in recess not being exactly where required in relation to the outer surfaces of the head. Castings compared with their patterns will sometimes show some inexplicable discrepancies! The machined out interiors of a cylinder head for twin cylinders are shown very well in the photograph of one of the Mastiff engine heads, Fig. 10.

The same photograph shows the preferred shape of the cylinder head interior according to reasonably modern ideas. A side valve head always tends to be somewhat straggly in respect of gas paths and combustion areas. This is one of the reasons why the roof of the combustion space should come fairly close down on to the top of the piston for at least part of the piston diameter. This reduces the volume of the space and makes for a slightly higher compression ratio than would otherwise be possible. A rather more important reason though, is that the very shallow space between the piston crown and the roof at T.D.C. promotes turbulence in the cylinder full of mixture and encourages gas flow to and from the valves.

Some degree of turbulence is desirable in the mixture both to ensure thorough mixing and the maximum rate of travel of the flame throughout the mixture, once combustion has started. When the combustion starts in one place with the spark, the greater turbulence there is in the mixture surrounding the plug points, the faster will the flame be spread throughout the mixture. In a model engine, with the small sizes and distances involved, the time available for the mixture to get well burning and develop some useful pressure on the piston before it has retreated down the cylinder is very small indeed—a matter of milliseconds only. Slower burning mixture conditions can be offset to some extent by advancing the ignition timing, but the disadvantage of this is that with ignition starting a very long way before T.D.C., some pressure is being developed before the piston has passed T.D.C. and can take advantage of it. Furthermore, such an extreme degree of advance will not suit slower running, such as might occur in getting a high-speed boat away, for instance.

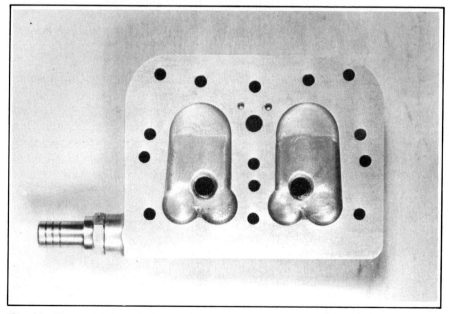

Fig. 10. The underside of one Mastiff cylinder head, showing two machined out combustion spaces.

The effect of lowering part of the combustion chamber roof to come comparatively close down on to the piston is to cause the piston, as it nears the top of its compression stroke to squeeze the compressed charge quite vigorously out from between itself and the roof in the general direction of the valves and plug. Hence the general term "squish" heads. Providing this effect is not overdone–and like most things, it can be!–it helps scavenging of that part of the head not directly above the piston, and urges a body of fresh mixture towards the plug, making for efficient and certain ignition.

Note the phrase "urges a body of mixture towards the plug". This, of course, is providing the plug is somewhere near the position which it is shown occupying in the Mastiff head. A side valve head is particularly suitable for placing the plug almost anywhere, so it may as well be sited in the place best suited to the plug itself and to what it has to do.

In a hot-running full size engine, it is sometimes found that the best place for the plug is quite near the exhaust valve. This is because by starting ignition of the mixture at the hottest point, detonation, or spontaneous ignition of part of the mixture is avoided. This can occur if the ignition is started at the coolest part of the head, when the pressure wave resulting from the ignition starts to further compress that part of the mixture already well heated from being trapped in the hottest part of the head.

However, conditions like this, where the temperatures are not so high and a much larger proportionate area of cooler metal encloses the charge, almost never apply in a model engine. Therefore the placing of the plug can be based on other considerations. The three main ones are: (1) the health of the plug itself, (2) the position that best ensures certainty of ignition, and (3) the position that provides the shortest reasonable flame path to the furthest extremity of the head. Considerations 1 and 2 both point to placing the plug quite near the inlet valve; the new cool charge sweeping over the plug points will materially help in keeping the plug cool, and the points will be surrounded by the new charge undiluted as far as possible by the products of the previous firing. So far as No. 3 consideration goes, the position that gives the shortest flame path is right in the middle of the head. However, the benefits arising from locating the plug much nearer the inlet valve rather outweigh this, making that the best position on balance. After all, almost everything is something of a compromise.

To return to the original point on machining S.V. heads, if the internal shape is to be milled out, then here is a case where a holding lug on the top of the casting could be of value in setting it up for milling. This could well be placed where the plug hole will be required, then the final machining operation would be to machine flat the rough stump of the sawn-off boss, and drill and tap it for the plug. Here too, it could pay to make the boss square in section. This could quickly be filed to produce parallel sides, which would simplify holding it in a machine vice for example, perhaps on the vertical slide, so that it could be passed across an end mill in two paths at right angles to each other.

In water cooled S.V. heads, the conventional way of arranging these is to make the water space a cast-in shape on the top of the head, and to machine out the internal shape underneath. The top water space wall, and any holding down stud pads or pillars are faced across so as to provide true and flat surfaces for a cover plate to bear on. The plate may be seated on the head proper either just by being held by the cylinder head nuts with a metal-to-metal joint, on a thin gasket, or by actually cementing it to the head surface. There is a lot to be said for this last

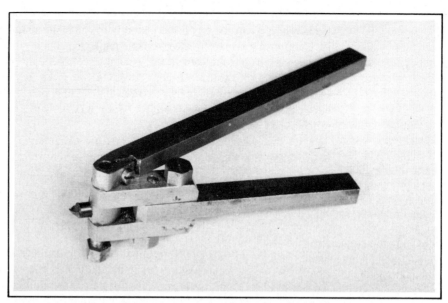

Fig. 11. Swing lathe tool for turning the internal shape of hemispherical cylinder heads. The inserted tool is swung by hand by means of the long top lever.

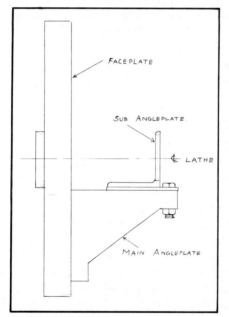

Fig. 12. Angleplate set-up for machining hemispherical heads.

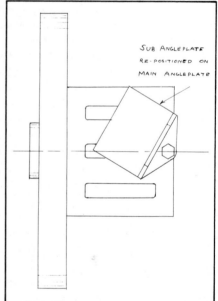

Fig. 13. Set-up for machining valve ports and seatings.

course, as once the essential machined surfaces of the head have been dealt with, there is rarely any need for the head proper and its cover plate to be separated again.

The cover plate for a water cooled head could also be provided with a chucking boss, but as there is rarely any machining on this required other than facing both sides, this can be dealt with quite well in the four-jaw chuck unless the edges are exceptionally thin.

O.H.V. cylinder heads are necessarily somewhat more complex, although here again most of them start as light alloy castings. Owing to the presence of the valves, considerably more machining is required on the casting to provide for inlet and exhaust ports, valve guides, seatings, and some sort of mounting points for the valve operating gear. Patterns can be built up for these in just the same way as for S.V. heads—it is just a question of fitting in and adding more bits. It is most essential however, to keep an eye on how the pattern will be withdrawn from the moulding sand, so that it *is* possible to lift it out without trapping any sand and destroying the mould.

As in the case of S.V. heads, it is preferable on most counts to machine in whatever shape is required for the under surface. In the case of vertically disposed valves, this will just amount to plain facing. With a hemispherical shaped "roof" to the head, this involves shaping the surface with a swinging lathe tool, Fig. 11. The turning for this part of the machining can be carried out with the head held in the chuck. When it comes to the drilling of the ports in the valve seat region, and perhaps turning in chamfered valve seats or recessing for inserted seatings, then a rather more elaborate holding fixture is required. This takes the shape of a small special angle plate—most easily made up from a short piece of steel angle—which in turn is mounted on a main angle plate attached to the lathe faceplate. If this sort of machining operation will be required, then it pays to hold the head on such a fixture for all the machining carried out on the under side. Fig. 12 shows the main requirements. The head is attached to the "sub angle plate" by its own holding down bolt holes and on finish turning the concave under surface, the fixture plate is swung round on the main angle plate to the correct angle for drilling the holes for valve guides and the lower ends of the ports. Note that the fixture plate must be attached to the main angle plate so that it swings about the centre point of the radius to which the head recess has been turned. Unless this condition is met, the holes, which will lie along the centre lines of the valves, will not meet the curved inner surface at the correct angles. Fig. 13 should make this clear.

Where it is desired to keep the compression ratio reasonably high, it can be awkward to machine hemispherical heads in a multi. If the design results in a long engine, then it may not be possible to arrange a convenient fixture to swing the head casting to machine the end cylinder heads, nor may it be possible to do this owing to the overhanging end of the head casting being too long to swing in the lathe. In the case of the 4 c.c. 4 cylinder baby engine, this was too small for it to be done without great difficulty. In cases like this, the valves can generally be located in a shallow machined trough, utilising vertically disposed valves, but minimising the size of the compression space necessary for valve clearance over the piston with a flat-faced head. This was done with the 4 c.c. engine as shown in Fig. 14 where midway along the valve trough a small angled flat face has been machined to accommodate the spark plug. A somewhat similar design is employed in the Westbury "Sealion" 4 cyl. O.H.C. engine of 30 c.c.

Like almost any other part of an engine, a head casting can be in some other metal than light alloy. Successful engines have been produced employing gunmetal heads—both S.V. and O.H.V. There is something to be said for this from the point of view of suitability of material for valve seatings and valve guides, if these are to be of the head metal itself. The main disadvantages are that it is very heavy, and at the moment, discouragingly expensive.

If weight is of no consequence, then cast iron has much to commend it. It is certainly much cheaper! The 1 c.c. engine shown in Fig. 1 has a cast iron head. In this case the head is not a casting, but the shape was fabricated from two pieces of cast iron, silver soldered together. Both pieces were machined from the solid from cast iron stick. Fig. 15 gives a clear idea of how the head was put together. The main part of the head was turned to produce a symmetrical finned shallow cylinder, such as a compression ignition two-stroke might use for a head. A square bottom slot, 5/16 in. wide, was then milled right across the top, and into this the "boomerang" shaped flat piece was silver soldered. This latter piece was shaped up from a slice off the same bar which produced the circular part of the head. After silver soldering together, the complete head was drilled and further machined where necessary exactly as if it had been a casting.

Cast iron is ideal material for valve seats, and in an iron head, the obvious thing is to machine the seats in the metal of the head itself. Furthermore, at the same setting in the lathe, the ports can be drilled and the holes reamed for inserting the valve guides. These too, can be of cast iron, with the advantage not only of good wearing properties, but the fact that they will expand and contract to the same extent as the head itself means that they are unlikely to come loose in service.

The question of valve seats is one where the type adopted comes down very much to one of personal preference. Many successful engines have been built with the valves seating direct on seats machined in the light alloy of the head material. Others have had separate seats in ring form, turned from somewhat harder or tougher material, pressed into machined recesses, thereby following car engine practice. Having said that this is a question of personal choice, may I say that I do not care for seating valves direct on light alloy. Apart from general wear and hammering from the valve, any abrasive bits of carbon together with the fact that the exhaust valve seat is probably the hottest part of the engine, could make for a short gastight life for the seat, partly depending on the alloy used. While an inserted seat of more suitable material would no doubt be considerably better, there are still disadvantages here too. The seat ring must be machined absolutely concentric and of an even thickness to close limits, or the valve will not seat gastight. It has to be pressed into place with equal precision for the same reason. Here, as with the inserted cylinder liner in a jacket of light alloy, different expansion co-efficients should be borne in mind. In both cases, given that the seatings are all that could be desired, the gas tightness of the valve will still depend on accurate machining and fitting of the separate valve guide. Here yet again, two different materials of different expansion rates will be involved.

On all counts I much prefer a combined tubular valve seat and guide—as a personal opinion, let me emphasise. The advantages of this form of construction are several. It can be made of a suitable material, and amounts to a straightforward turning and drilling job, with all the necessary concentric operations carried out at the one setting in the chuck. If something *should* go wrong, then you will only be scrapping one tiny item. Its housing in the head is a large diameter plain through hole, which can be D-bitted or reamed for an exact size and good finish. No separate valve guide is involved, having to be accurately aligned with the seating. The contact area of such a component in the bore of the head is a much larger area than the total of inserted ring seat and valve guide, which means that it will be secure with a lighter press fit, or what is probably better still, it can be made an easy slip fit and Loctited in position. The gas tightness of the valve is quite independent of any standard of fit in the head. Lastly, the whole thing at its biggest diameter need be no larger than the diameter of the valve head, which would be

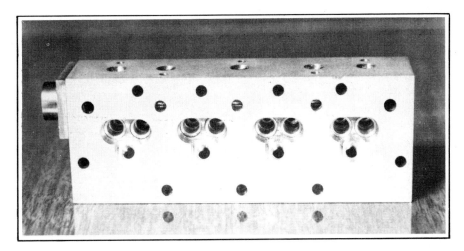

Fig. 14. Underside of the 4 c.c. 4 cylinder engine head, showing valve and plug dispositions.

Fig. 15. The fabricated construction of the 1 c.c. O.H.V. cylinder head.

almost the diameter of a machined seating; it would be distinctly less than that of a substantial seat ring. The valve cage—for that is what it amounts to—is quite easily precisely located in the head by inserting it till a small top flange on which the valve spring will bear, contacts the outer end of the housing in the head. Drilling the inlet and exhaust passages into the ports immediately under the valve head is carried out after the combined seats and guides have been fixed in the head.

The Mastiff engine was fitted with this type of combined seat and guide, turned from dural, and these have given every satisfaction so far. The S.V. engine Fig. 3 and the O.H.V. one Fig. 1 both have this type of guide and seating, only in these

41

cases they are of cast iron which have given equally good service. All these were lightly pressed in.

It should be obvious that an important factor affecting the proper seating of the valve, and consequently its gas tightness, is the nicety of the fit of the valve stem in the guide. It should naturally not be unduly tight, nor should it be slack at all. If there is any undesirable amount of clearance the valve will be free to move sideways very slightly, and so cannot be depended on to seat squarely on to the seating directly it contacts it. This state of affairs is unavoidably aggravated by the distance from the valve seat to the inner end of the valve guide. This distance is often quite considerable in relation to the sizes of the components involved, and there is generally little that can be done to reduce it. The only positive thing that will help here is to make the guide as long as possible. A long guide will not only control the direction of the valve's travel more effectively, but will help reduce the possibility of air leaks round the valve stem—particularly desirable in the case of the inlet valve—and result in a longer life for the guide through providing a larger bearing surface. This is a factor assuming greater importance in the case of overhead valves, where the "stroking" of the rocker end on the valve stem tends to try to tilt the valve during its travel.

To express another personal opinion, I think most published engine designs would benefit from distinctly longer valve guides, for the reasons given above. Some of these, being intended as high performance engines, have a fairly big valve lift; here the tilting action of the rocker would be bigger still, in proportion to the valve lift, unless the rocker arm was disproportionately long.

The length of unsupported valve stem under the head in the port was mentioned above, and another point arises here. It is desirable, in any engine, to try as far as can be arranged to keep the gas flow through the ports and passages to a uniform speed. Variation in the gas speed for a constant engine speed can have bad effects on the mixture, a sudden increase in the area of the passage slowing down the gas flow momentarily and tending to throw the fuel out of suspension into liquid droplets. Conversely, a sudden reduction in area requires the gas flow to speed up, introducing a restriction to the free flow and tending to reduce the volume slightly at full throttle conditions through the intertia of the gas column, and its consequent reluctance to vary its speed.

Where the mixture flows freely along a passage of uniform area into the port— also of the same area—there will occur just such a restriction through the presence of the valve stem reducing the effective area of the port. The remedy for this is to enlarge the diameter of the port in that part from the inner end of the valve guide to the valve seat. The smaller the engine, the more this is likely to take effect, owing to the proportionately thicker valve stem. If we take a look at some elementary figures about it, the remedy involves such a very small adjustment that it is probably worth adopting even on engines intended for quite moderate performance.

Consider the case of an engine having ports and passages of 5/16 in. bore, with valves have 1/8 in. dia. stems. The area of the 5/16 in. port is .0767 sq. ins. The cross sectional area of the 1/8 in. valve stem is .01227 squ. ins. It is obvious that the port area will be reduced by this amount in that part where the valve stem comes. So what is needed is the area of the port housing the valve stem to be increased by the amount of the valve stem sectional area, i.e., .0767 + .01227 = .08897 sq. ins. Now, what diam. does the port need to be made to have that area? You can calculate it out easily enough, but it is much simpler to refer to tables. From these, it is quickly seen that a circle of 21/64 in. diam. has an area of .0847 sq. ins., and that of a 11/32 in. circle is .0928. The difference in port diameter necessary to cancel out completely the presence of the valve stem is thus seen to be surprisingly small, and the 21/64 in. bore would be quite adequate. Even in a cylinder head where room is at a premium, this very slight increase should be accommodated without difficulty.

We could have a look at some other points having a bearing on this when we come to consider the valves themselves.

Applying water cooling to O.H.V. cylinder heads is a bit more complicated than it is with side valves. This is naturally brought about by the larger number of essential bits present on the O.H.V. head as compared with the S.V. version. Generally the most convenient way is basically the same as with side valves— casting in the water spaces on the top, and then covering them in with a separate plate. Owing to the presence of valve guide seatings and possible mounting points for valve rockers, the water spaces assume much more devious shapes, so that cast-in cavities may in some cases have to be supplemented by a little machining. This can arise when the desired final shape cannot be cast in a straightforward mould. The extra machining here is often most easily carried out with the aid of things like coarse dental drills or tiny specially made chisels, often used freehand. These are cases where "the end justifies the means", and if a quite unorthodox method produces the desired result—well, good luck!

This sort of awkwardness extends to the water space cover plate, where it may have to be fancifully shaped, or feature cut-outs at strategic points to slip over projections forming part of the head. Sometimes the necessary additions of this sort to the head itself can be turned to advantage where valve cages, for example, could be made slightly longer and fitted after the cover plate is in place, the cages serving to hold the plate in position. Things like the feet of a rocker shaft column can sometimes be used to spread a bolting pressure over the light alloy plate, which might otherwise distort around the points where such pressure might be applied by a plain nut and washer. Every projected engine can only have such points worked out in the manner most suited to the individual design, in conjunction with any other features having a bearing on it.

The 4 cyl. baby engine head gets round this question by what amounts to side-stepping it. The head here—Fig. 14—is machined from the solid, with no shaped water spaces or cover plate. So the water ways, such as they are, are merely holes of as large a diameter as could be accommodated, drilled through the length of the head either side of the valves, and having connecting holes drilled up from the underside to connect them to the water jackets round the cylinder liners in the block. This, of course, results in a very much smaller water capacity in the head, but as really tiny engines generally run fairly cool, it should at least help keep the temperature down a little round the valves. Whether it really helps materially or not, the engine has shown no sign of overheating so far.

As regards the internal shape of O.H.V. cylinder heads, formerly, and now again more recently, the flat surface head with vertical valves is favoured for moderate performance general purpose engines. From the model engineering point of view, this makes for easy and straightforward machining—which is always a worthwhile point. It is also claimed to be reasonably efficient as compared with any other shape.

From the volumetric efficiency point of view it is not as good as the hemispherical head. For a given volume of mixture in a closed vessel, the shape that will

43

contain it with the smallest surface area is a sphere. It is desirable in a high efficiency engine to minimise the surface area exposed to the flame so as to reduce the amount of heat lost to the cooling air or water via the area of metal exposed to the burning mixture. All the heat so transmitted is wasted, as it is not applied to heating—and so expanding—the volume of gas resulting from the combustion.

If it were possible to contain the whole cylinder full of gas in a perfect sphere, formed half by the hemispherical head and the other half by a hemispherical concave piston crown, then you would have the minimum area exposed to the source of heat. However, due to normal engine proportions, this would result in a very low compression ratio, and so while the hemispherical head half could very well be retained, the piston is generally flat-topped—or nearly so. Some car engines offer a choice of compression ratios, the high compression version having a flat topped piston, while the low compression one has a slightly concave piston crown. At the other extreme, a number of engines have a hemispherical head in con-junction with a domed piston top. This is generally to produce a really high com-pression ratio, and at the same time to take advantage of the other favourable features offered by the hemispherical head.

In the case of a hemispherical head having two sizeable valves, they each take up a fair proportion of the head area, and so their stems naturally have to be inclined away from each other in order to have the heads seating on a ring normal to the surface of the head. This valve angle, depending on the degree of concavity of the head, can be anything up to about 60 degrees, and makes for the inclusion of other features tending to efficiency. For one thing, if the centre line of the ports is horizontal, then the gas flow does not have to be suddenly deflected through 90 degrees just under the valve head, but only through 60 deg. In a model the inclination of the valves can mean that slightly larger valves can be accom-modated than would be possible in a flat surface head fitting the same bore cylinder. In a full size engine, there is nothing like the battle to house big enough valves, because the plug is so much smaller in proportion. In a model engine, the plug can easily take up one third of the cylinder diameter at the expense of the equally essential valves.

A model engine could also benefit probably from the greater distance between the outer ends of the valve stems, providing more room for valve gear and rockers. The rockers might be slightly lengthened, reducing the side load on the valve stems through flattening the arc of the swing of the rockers at their point of contact with the valve stem.

In a flat head moderate compression ratio engine, the space between the head surface and the piston top is generally enough to provide for the thickness of the valve head and its movement off its seat when the piston is at T.D.C. In the hemi-spherical head, the outer edge of the head will come much closer to the piston than would any part of a flat head surface, which means that the valve will also be closer to the piston. When you take into account the fact that the hemispherical head normally features on fairly high performance engines, and therefore that the valve timing is likely to make use of a fair degree of valve overlap, the valves are likely to be further off their seats at T.D.C. than those in a more moderate performance flat head engine. This often means that the piston crown has to be specially shaped to afford clearance to the nearest edges of the valves at T.D.C. Indeed, it is not unknown for one or both of the valves to hit the piston crown in a sports car engine, if this is revved a bit ham-fistedly, especially if the valve springs should happen to be a bit on the weak side and lost a little of their pristine liveliness.

In a model engine, clearances sufficient to guard against this sort of event can become quite critical, and like so many other things are largely a matter of compromise. On this particular point, it is better on the whole to avoid having to modify the shape of the piston top with notches and scooped-out shapes for two reasons: first, the piston crown may have to be made thick enough in the first place to allow of machining out the necessary depression, making for a heavy piston, and secondly, a perfectly symmetrical piston will not distort out of round under heat to anything like the extent that an odd shaped one might.

This question of cylinder head interior shapes is closely tied in with that of compression ratios. To get a reasonable power output from a given engine, the compression ratio needs to be fairly high. But this is also directly related to the type of engine it is, and the purpose for which it is intended. Compromise again! For instance, it would be quite wrong to have the highest possible compression ratio on a model horizontal gas engine, as indeed it would on a leisurely revving side valve engine for general interest running. An efficiently designed O.H.V. engine for say, a boat required to have a nicely brisk performance could well have a compression ratio distinctly higher than those of the two previously mentioned examples, while a purely racing engine might well have the ratio pushed as high as can be handled.

As you might expect, there are pros and cons for both ends of the range. The high compression engine is almost invariably a high speed, high performance engine, and so can be expected to exhibit the characteristics that naturally go with its nature. It will not be the easiest of starters, through needing some effort to swing it over T.D.C. against the high degree of compression; this is aggravated by the need for as fast a cranking speed as possible on starting because of the big ports and therefore lower gas speed at cranking speed. The valve timing on a really high speed engine is not generally conducive to nice slow speed running, so that its cranking and starting speeds come at the worst end of its performance. Ignition timing and carburettor settings may also both need some variation for a good start from those settings which enable it to run happily at its best speed.

With the low compression, more "woolly" engine, while it will take kindly to the starting speed applied, carburation can be critical, as any falling-off in the carburettor's performance could well mean that the engine does not get sufficient of the right mixture for its much more gentle power stroke to get it going. At low speeds too, any little thing like a slightly leaky valve or inlet valve stem, or perhaps a poorly fitting piston will show up to much greater effect than in the higher speed engine.

The high compression engine is generally much more "touchy" all round, and can earn itself the reputation of being something of an awkward beast. The remedy for that is to keep it all times nicely adjusted and well tuned up, and to get to know its little foibles thoroughly.

It is not too easy to lay down hard and fast rules as to what is a suitable compression ratio. I suppose one could roughly classify things and say that an engine having a compression ratio of around 5 or 6 : 1 was distinctly low. The medium performance engine might fall in the range of 6 : 1 to 8 : 1, while the real high performance job could boast a few points higher-up to say 9 or 10 : 1. These, on normal fuels available from the pump.

It is not at all easy to calculate what the exact compression ratio will be, when the engine is at the "on paper" stage. You can run through a few figures and get a rough idea, but that is about all. The flat head O.H.V. type is about the easiest, although even here, such things as the thickness of the valve heads in the combustion space and any slight recessing there might be at the plug points can combine to make the actual result something different to the calculated one. The actual ratio, of course, is the ratio between the total volume of the cylinder at B.D.C. and that at T.D.C. If you want to arrive at an exact figure, the best thing is to calculate it as nearly as you can and arrange for the construction of the engine to provide for some slight variation by the insertion of a gasket under the head to lower the ratio, or to skim a fraction off the end of the cylinder barrel to raise it. The actual volume can be measured from the completed engine, and such adjustments carried out as may be necessary.

The practical side of the measurement is quite simple to carry out, and the only piece of equipment necessary is a small disposable plastic hypodermic syringe. The little 2 ½ c.c. size is very suitable, this being calibrated in tenths of c.c's.

Remove the plug and turn the engine to exactly top dead centre. Tilt the engine so that the plug hole is uppermost. Charge the syringe with exactly 2 ½ c.c. of thin oil; something like "Three-in-One" is very suitable. Gently fill up the combustion space with oil through the plug hole, being careful not to overfill and lose any oil, till the oil level is just at the bottom of the plug hole. Make a careful note of the exact quantity of oil it takes. Turn the engine to bring the piston to bottom dead centre and again fill it up, again noting exactly how much oil had to be added. From your notes of these two quantities you now have all the necessary data to work out the compression ratio. We said that the ratio was that between the volumes at B.D.C. and T.D.C. You have a note of what it was at T.D.C., and the total of that and the extra that had to be added gives the volume at B.D.C. So just dividing the smaller into the larger gives the required figure. Note that in the case of say, a 10 c.c. engine, the total volume will work out to more than 10 c.c. This is quite in order, as the nominal 10 c.c. of engine capacity is the swept volume, i.e., the volume found experimentally at B.D.C. will be greater than this by the volume of the combustion space above the piston, this amount having to be added to the swept volume for the figure of total volume. That all sounds like a lot of volumes—but it is all quite straightforward if you ever come to do it.

4 Valves, Valve Gears

While the factors affecting the accommodation of the valves in an O.H.V. cylinder head were set out in that chapter, the valves themselves were taken pretty much for granted. So let us now take a look at some of the points applying to the valves themselves as components.

Valves, in my own experience, need to have every possible care taken in their production if trouble is to be avoided in use. It comes down almost entirely to a matter of careful lathe work. The whole thing needs to have a good finish, the head and stem must be absolutely concentric, and the stem must be exactly parallel and a perfect fit in its guide.

Mild steel—especially the freecutting sort—is not really the best material for petrol engine valves, although it is admittedly the first thought. It is not too resistant to the corrosive atmosphere inside the engine, and it very easily rusts in the warm water vapour present in the cylinder at the end of a short run. The small diameter stem too, if it is of the type that receives the direct impact of a tappet or rocker, is soon spread and distorted to the point where the spring anchorage fixture is troublesome to remove.

A much better choice of material than mild steel is stainless steel— and this *can* be of the freecutting variety. I have never had any trouble with valves made from this through unsuitability of material. It can be machined just as easily as ordinary mild steel and if anything, produces a better finish when the lathe tools are in proper condition.

It is unusual nowadays to some across valves made in two pieces, a stem with separate head brazed on. This was not uncommon years ago, particularly for the larger low-speed model gas engines, but present day model engines call for something a bit better than that. This means that a one-piece valve can only be turned from the solid rod. Of course, the head could be roughly formed with some blacksmithing work on a rod slightly bigger than the finished stem diameter and the whole thing machined from there, but I have never heard of this being done.

A source of material I have used in the past is the local garage. If you talk nicely to the service manager, he will generally produce several large car or lorry valves, and the stems of these are generally of sufficient diameter from which to turn a complete model valve. A valve so obtained can be a complete write-off so far as the vehicle it came from is concerned,—scaled and burnt seatings, worn or warped stems, bruised and mangled cotter grooves, and still provide plenty of usable material for a baby valve or two. However, having said all that, let me add that on the whole I don't think it is worth it!

This is chiefly because the steel from which full size valves are made— particularly exhausts—is extremely tough to turn, so that it is not easy to get a nice finish on a really parallel stem as small as we are likely to want them. Full size valves lead a much harder life than do those in a model engine, so that the ability to stand up to hours of nearly red-hot working under heavy pressures is not a virtue that is essential in our much smaller engines.

So it comes down to turning the valve complete from a rod of head diameter, or slightly larger. The easiest and conventional way of doing this is to chuck the rod with sufficient material protruding from the chuck to allow of machining the whole of the stem and the seat face, parting off near the chuck to leave enough full diameter on the stem to provide the head. In this way, all the essential diameters can be dealt with at the one setting, making for concentricity right through. The stem, long before it is reduced to finished diameter, will need support from the tail centre. This can be provided either with the conventional pointed centre or with a female centre; a half-centre of whichever type is used providing a bit more room for manoeuvring the turning tool. The stem needs to be turned slightly over long, to allow for cutting away the extreme end to lose the drilled centre hole or the pointed end that may have been used with a female centre.

The seating face on valves is normally turned to an angle of 45 degrees, and this is accepted as universal practice sufficiently widely for it to be taken as normal practice for model engine valves also. The seating should be turned by movement of the tool along a path at 45 degrees to the axis of the valve, and not by presenting a 45 deg. angled tool to the edge of the valve head.

In deciding the sizes for model valves, there crops up the question of stem diameter. In my own case, this generally comes down to a case of how the valve spring will be anchored. If a reasonably high performance engine is best served by a valve having a separate cotter seating in a groove round the valve stem, then the stem obviously cannot be too small in diameter, or the cotter will be too minute for the job, and the stem diameter at the bottom of the groove will also be dangerously small. A point to bear in mind here is that the stem diameter where it works in the guide can often be larger than is strictly desirable for the stem just under the head, where it may take up an undesirable amount of room in the port. A way out in that case is to make the working part of the stem as large as reasonable, and then to neck the stem down under the head for that part of the stem housed in the port.

In most cases the stem will be disproportionately large in relation to the head diameter compared with a full size valve. A valve of head diameter of 3/8 or 5/16 say, could well have a stem of 1/8 in. dia., with the top part of the stem necked down to 3/32 in. or so. In the baby 4 cylinder engine, the valves have a head diameter of 3/16 in., with 3/32 in. dia. stems necked down to 1/16 in. over the port portion. I would think this is about as small as one could safely go for valves operating at anything like moderate to high speeds, with stiffish springs.

So with a valve stem diameter to a large extent dependent on how the spring is to be anchored, how *is* it to be fixed? There are several different ways of doing it, and the choice will largely be dictated by the overall size of the valve and the sort of duty it will be called on to perform. The drawing, Fig. 16 shows some of the ways in which it has been successfully done.

Fixture "A" is the old original way, where the valve stem was drilled across for a pin, the pin being trapped in a recess in the bottom of the spring collar. This is almost never seen now but was quite widely used at one time, especially for big valves with a large diameter stem such as might be used in gas engines. It is obviously not very suitable for a high speed engine, nor for a small model engine having a small diameter stem in the first place.

Sketch "B" shows a modern development of this, and I have used this with every success on valves with stems down to 1/8 in. diam. In this case, the pin is superseded by a roughly horse-shoe shaped cotter, fitting closely round a square bottomed groove turned in the stem. The cotter is in fact a slotted washer, the slot being just wide enough to allow of slipping the cotter over the smaller diameter at the bottom of the groove in the valve stem. It is a neat fixing, provides a secure anchorage, and the groove in the stem does not have to be all that deep. If the cotter is made of silver steel (unhardened) or something a bit tougher than mild steel, it should prove entirely satisfactory. The valve springs in Mastiff are anchored in this way.

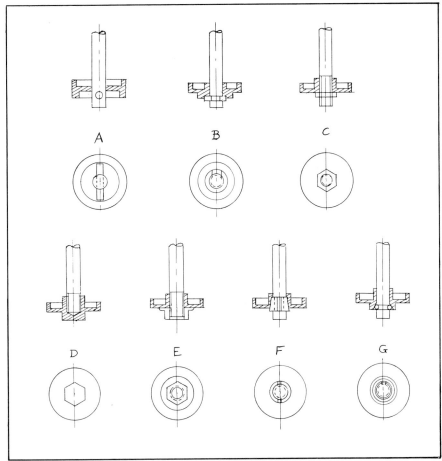

Fig. 16. Some valve stem fixtures for springs.

For really small stems, where the strength of the stem at the bottom of a groove might be a bit doubtful, there is much to be said for some form of screwed fitting. Sketch "C" shows the simplest. Here the bottom of the stem is threaded and the collar tapped for a shakeless fit on the thread. A thin locknut below the collar prevents the collar unscrewing in service. One possible disadvantage of this type of fixture is that the extreme end of the stem is slightly reduced in diameter on account of the thread, just where it comes in for hammering from the rocker tip or tappet.

If this is looked on as a drawback grave enough to be avoided, then it can be dodged by using the type shown at "D". This is again a screwed stem, but here the

49

collar is made deeper so as to provide sufficient depth for a blind hole, tapped to fit the threaded stem. This version could be hardened, giving the benefit of good wearing properties. It needs to be screwed tightly to the bottom of the thread to avoid the risk of it coming unscrewed.

Type "E" is very similar, with the difference that it is in two parts—the tapped collar and a separate locknut below. The nut here is made considerably thicker than a simple locknut would need to be for two reasons; one is so that the stem can be made short enough not to come fully through the nut to the outer surface, so that all the wear comes on the lower face of the nut. If the nut is hardened—or case hardened—the contact surface will wear well, leaving the actual valve stem untouched. The other reason for the deepish nut is that if the valve stem is well short of the tappet or rocker, there is a slight amount of movement up or down the screwed stem available for valve clearance adjustment. In the case of a side valve engine, this does away with the separate provision for tappet clearance adjustment on the tappets, thus saving weight and room. It will be noticed that the 3 ½ c.c. S.V. engine has this sort of valve spring fixture, and it has consistently worked well on this engine.

Note that if a spring collar screwing on to the valve stem with a locknut is used, then the collar must be provided with at least two spanner flats so that the locknut can be pulled up tight enough to lock. In the case of the 1 c.c. O.H.V. engine, the collar was pared down to the minimum amount of metal and four flats provided which actually cut into the spring recess. This just leaves four wide fingers to locate the spring, while reducing the weight of the collar as far as possible. This can be clearly seen in Fig. 15.

Looking at type "F", this is a plain copy of the modern car type fixture. I have not used this on a model engine myself, but there is no reason at all why this should not be perfectly successful on a valve stem big enough to accept a usable groove. Possible disadvantages might be the slightly more elaborate machining required to make the split tapered cotters, and perhaps more fiddling required in the actual fitting to the engine—particularly if this were a S.V. engine, where access could be more restricted than on an O.H.V. engine.

Type "G" is a simplification of type "F", in which the split tapered cotter is replaced by a spring wire circlip. This was used in the American "Morton" 5 cyl. radial aero engine, which had valve stems of .092 in. dia., the groove being only 8 thous. deep. The circlip was of 28 S.W.G. piano wire, the 30 deg. taper hole in the collar jamming the circlip tight, providing a secure fixing. A good design point here is that the groove round the valve stem is of semicircular shape, avoiding the sharp corners of a square-bottom groove. Here again, I have not used this type myself, being not too sure how one could ensure that home-made circlips would clench completely closed, as would be necessary to ensure that they seated right home in their grooves before the collars pinched them under the pressure of the valve springs.

The examples shown do not necessarily include every possible type, and you may well be able to work out something different that suits your particular engine better. However, just to recap., I have had every satisfaction from type "E" for very small stems, and from "B" for somewhat larger ones.

As the methods of anchoring valve springs are naturally closely linked to the springs themselves, what is there to consider about springs?

For a start, it is often possible to find a size of commercially produced spring that fits in very well for a particular engine design. The advantage of the commer-

50

cially produced spring over the home made one is that the commercial one is wound to correct shape and size first, and then heat treated to give the bounce. This results in a spring that has never been stressed at all before it is put into service. With the home made version, while you can wind this to the exact size you want, the already heat treated wire is in fact being distorted to make it take up the shape required. This is said to be something of a drawback to the home made spring, but I confess I have never come across any obvious evidence of it, and all my valve springs have been wound up in the lathe on a simple rod mandrel from spring steel wire. By making your own you can experiment with mandrel sizes, gauges of wire, and pitch of turns until you come up with something that is just what is required.

It is useful to note here that the strength of the finally shaped spring is not only dependent on the gauge of the wire, but also on the number of turns. The spring having the greater number of turns will be more lively on the whole, and can provide a more uniform pressure over the required valve movement than one having fewer turns. It will also need less force to compress it a given amount. A larger number of turns for a given length obviously means that they must be closer pitched, and it equally obviously will not do to have the pitch so fine that there is danger of the turns contacting each other when the valve lifts.

Modern car valve springs are mostly fitted in duplicate; that is, the normal spring has a smaller spring inside it. This serves two purposes. Anything which can spring or vibrate at all will have a natural "resonant frequency" of vibration. This means in simple terms that if something free to vibrate slightly suffers a blow so as to set it vibrating, it will vibrate at the same speed every time. Flicking a glass with the finger nail illustrates this. If something is so vibrating at its own natural frequency, and the vibrations are maintained by feeding in vibrations from some external source *at the same frequency*, then the vibrations will build up to a considerable force. Powerful singers have been reputed to be able to shatter a wineglass by singing a sustained note at it of the glass's natural resonant frequency; soldiers are often ordered to break step when marching over a slender bridge. Both these are cases of build-up of vibrations at a resonant frequency. In the case of car valve springs, they are subject to recurring flexings of considerable amplitude over a wide range of speeds, from low speed up to speeds high enough to reach the resonant frequency of the fair mass of the spring. When this happens, the spring is vibrating on its own to the extent that it cannot maintain the pressure it should on the valve, so the valve fails to shut down completely on its seating. This, just when the engine is probably being called on to put out its maximum power.

A somewhat similar effect results from "valve bounce", although this does not arise from the same cause. Here, the spring is too weak to compel the tappet to exactly follow the shape of the cam, and at high speeds the tappet gets left behind in mid-air as it were, when it should start to follow the closing curve of the cam.

The second small spring fitted inside the main one goes a long way towards curing both these effects, as it has a higher resonant frequency than the main spring —being smaller—and it also serves to augment the insufficient pressure of the main spring in following the cam contour at high speed.

In small model engines, it is unlikely that these effects will make themselves evident, as the weight of the valve is minute compared with the full size one, and the resonant frequency of the small spring will almost certainly be higher than the speed normally reached by the engine. One type of spring having certain advantages over the normal coil spring is the "hairpin" type of spring. The main part of the spring in this case is shaped much like a safety pin, with one or more turns of a powerful spring stood well out from the valve stem. An incidental advantage of this is that the valve stem and guide are much more exposed to cooling air than if they were in the centre of a coil spring, or pair of concentric coil springs. One big disadvantage of this type for model work is the large amount of room it needs on the head.

With reasonably proportioned single coil springs on model valves, there is little fear that some troubles will appear than can beset high speed full size engines. The most likely, on a really high speed engine, would be valve bounce, and this could probably be cured by increasing the spring pressure slightly—given that the valve gear is robust enough to cope with slightly heavier spring pressure. Let us just say that it should have been in the first place!

One practical way in which to check if valve bounce is really taking place when it is suspected, is to mark the cam with emery cloth scratches across the line of tappet travel, i.e., in line with the shaft. The engine is then run under load at high speed for a period and the cam can then be examined under a magnifying glass. If bounce is taking place, the scratches on the "downhill" side of the cam will be much more clearly visible than those where they will have been rubbed smooth by the tappet on the lift side, showing that there has been much less contact where the tappet has been skipping the cam flank.

As a rough guide on spring strengths for what it may be worth, the springs on the 1 c.c. O.H.V. engine need a pressure of 20 oz. to open the valve, while those on Mastiff need 3 lbs. The actual job of making valve springs by winding them up from spring steel wire is quite straightforward.

On the question of springs, it should be borne in mind that the valve spring is normally called on not only to return the valve firmly to its seating, but in S.V. engines to keep the tappet firmly in contact with the cam. In the case of an O.H.V. engine, it also has to tip the rocker back to the valve closed position and reverse the direction of the pushrod movement to maintain pressure on the tappet. To assist in this part of the job, springs are sometimes fitted to the rockers to keep them pressed back in the direction tending to compress the pushrod. While this lets the valve spring devote all its strength to closing the valve, the rocker gear is still called on to handle spring loads equal to the total of the pressures needed to compress both springs, and so should be amply stout enough to do this without being overloaded.

To digress slightly, the fancier flights of mathematics have been strictly excluded from this book. If you do happen to be something of a mathematician, that could be all to the good, and you may well find some useful application for these if you dig deeply enough. However, let's face it, we no not all have the ability to handle the sort of maths that looks like Chinese wallpaper, and a very elementary brand of mathematics can generally be made to furnish the information we want. This can often come in handy for verifying some fact that we may have been told, or for re-checking some item of data perhaps imperfectly remembered. This digression was prompted by being about to mention another factor affecting valves—a factor which might perhaps be thought to belong more properly to consideration of cams. That factor is the amount of valve lift.

When you come to think about it, the amount of lift of a valve must be related to its size, and to the size of the port associated with the valve. Those features decide the lift, and the cam is then designed to lift the valve the indicated amount. When the valve is fully open, it should provide as free a flow ideally to the gas through the port as if the valve were not there. This means that the area of the circular gap between the face of the valve and the seating should be not less than the area of the port below the valve. Surely this sounds like a constant related to port diameter?

And so it is—and we can say straightaway that this area of opening is produced when the valve has lifted a distance equal to 25% of the port diameter. Proof? Well, let's make use of some of that schoolboy arithmetic.

The port area, as everyone will know, is worked out from the formula πR^2. As —the radius—is half the diameter, this can be written $\frac{\pi D^2}{4}$. This area we want in the shape of a long thin rectangle, in which the length of the long side will be equal to the circumference of the port, while the little short side will represent the valve lift. The circumference of the port will be πD, which is the rectangle's long side. Therefore, dividing the area by the length of the long side to give the sort side we get $\frac{\pi D^2}{4} \div \pi D = \frac{D}{4}$. The short side (valve lift) is therefore $\frac{D}{4}$, ¼ of port diameter.

I suggested a little way back that the ideal condition would be to have the valve open sufficiently for its area to equal that of the port. While the calculated constant of $\frac{D}{4}$ ought to do this, two unavoidable factors tend to make this not wholly true. One of these is the presence of the valve stem altering the actual port area available for gas flow, if this is not adjusted as mentioned in the consideration of cylinder heads. The other is the presence of the valve head close to the seating, sharply diverting—and therefore to some extent, impeding—the free flow of the gas through the port. In practice these can be offset by applying the $\frac{D}{4}$ formula not to the port diameter, but to the valve diameter. This will have the effect of indicating a valve lift of slightly more than is theoretically needed, and should make sure that the valve does at least open enough.

In practice, it is surprising how small a valve lift suffices to pass a useable volume of gas. Really senior readers may remember seeing engines working fitted with an automatic inlet valve. I can—just! These had no inlet cams or valve gear at all, but just a valve spring weak enough to let the valve be sucked open by the piston descending on the inlet stroke. The succeeding compression power and exhaust strokes all held the valve shut. When such an engine was running, it was almost impossible to see any movement at all on the valve stem and spring; all you got was a rather rude sounding "raspberry" noise, as the valve buzzed on its seating every induction stroke.

While it was not to be compared in efficiency with the more modern cam controlled wider opening valve, it worked quite well in slow speed, largish engines.

One last little point on valves—grinding in. Not so long back, almost all valves were provided with a screwdriver slot in the middle of the head for this purpose. A variation of this was a couple of shallow holes, intended to be used with a sort of two-pronged key. However, it is desirable to avoid any sort of sharp or thin edges in the actual combustion space in any engine, as these can get hot enough to cause pre-ignition. So valves now normally have a completely smooth head surface. In the case of valves of car engine size, grinding-in can be carried out by the use of a rubber sucker attached to some convenient handle. Miniature model valves are not too easily held securely without damage for milling or sawing a slot, and the sharp edges of such a slot are equally to be avoided in a model engine as in a full size one. Model valves are too small too, to allow of using a rubber sucker.

Grinding in can quite effectively be carried out by using a small pin-chuck to grip the stem, pulling on the chuck to press the valve on the seat.

Note that grinding-in model valves should be restricted to the absolute minimum the softness of the material of both valve and seating compared with the full size versions means that comparatively little grinding will begin to produce circular scores round the valve face and seating. A leaky valve having these characteristics will never be made gas tight by further grinding, and by far the best course then is to re-face the valve in the lathe, and to make up a seating cutter tool with a guide stem nicely fitting the bore of the valve guide.

For bronze seatings, the procedure is sometimes advocated of going through the motions of grinding-in lightly, but doing it quite dry, which has the effect of burnishing the seating and removing any last trace of minute machining marks. This is purely a "touch-up" process of course, as no metal is actually removed from either surface.

Closely tied in with the subject of valves is the question of their operation, i.e. valve gears.

In a S.V. engine, this boils down to a single small component between the cam and the bottom of the valve stem—the tappet. This not only translates the shape of the rotating cam into straight-line movement to operate the valve, but has much larger bearing surfaces to take the side thrust of the cam. This is no more than a plain plunger, bearing on the cam at its lower end, contacting the valve stem at the top. It is normally made truly round and left free to rotate. The shape of the bottom end contacting the cam will depend on the cam, but where the end is plain, sliding on the cam, it is normally flat. It may well have a larger diameter foot, but where this is featured it is generally dictated by the need for a larger diameter to contact the cam than would be provided by a tappet of the same diameter throughout. (See chapter 5 on Cams). There is often the need to reduce the diameter for the greater part of the length through considerations of space or to save weight. Modern car engines mostly feature tappets parallel throughout, and of a fair diameter. In a model, if this results in a too solid and heavy slug of metal, it can be lightened by drilling out to make it a hollow cylinder—left closed at the bottom, of course. The top of the hole can be tapped for fitting a screw and locknut for adjusting valve clearance, or if the adjustment comes on the valve stem a hardened closing plug can be pressed in.

In a number of Westbury S.V. designs, the tappets were drilled and left open at the top, the tappet top rim contacting the hardened locknut of the valve spring fixture.

A useful design point, not always incorporated, is that the vertical centre line of the tappet can be located slightly to one side of the centre of the cam flank, so that the tappet is not exactly centrally disposed over the cam. The effect of this is to cause the tappet to rotate slowly when the engine is running, serving to equalise wear on the contact faces and largely avoiding the formation of a depressed area in the tappet head where it contacts the valve. Such an area can make clearance adjustment more a matter of guesswork than anything.

This same offsetting can also be applied to the relative locations of tappet and valve stem centre lines, in which case the axis of the tappet can "split the difference" between the offset distance of valve stem and cam centre.

It was particularly convenient to do this in Mastiff, where space between cams was at a premium through valves on opposite sides of the engine coming almost in line.

O.H.V. push rod engines also require tappets, although in this case it is rather the exception to find valve clearance adjustment on the tappets. Here, the tappet is generally a plain hollow affair, with the bottom of the central hole round ended to provide a seating for the ball-ended pushrod. The diameter of the hole is normally considerably larger than the diameter of the pushrod, which looks after any slight inclination there may be on the rod, and also the slight swing on the rod resulting from the top end swinging in a small arc to follow the rocker end movement. By seating the pushrod in the bottom of a deep hole, the tappet can be made lighter by the deep drilling, and at the same time a useful oil pocket is produced. The extra length of rod needed to reach the bottom of the hole would be lighter than the slug of metal removed by drilling the hole.

Pushrods need to be light but quite stiff. In comparatively short ones, silver steel rod shaped and hardened at each end is generally satisfactory. The 1 c.c. O.H.V. engine has pushrods made from short lengths of light alloy knitting needle, turned down slightly at each end to accept tiny hardened silver steel ferrules pressed on. This has worked very well, and one could assume that similar slightly thickened up rods should be equally effective on a bigger engine.

The top end of the pushrod engages with the rocker, and where it does so is a convenient point to introduce the clearance adjustment. All this needs to be is a short bolt having a head thick enough to accept a round bottomed socket drilled for the rod end and provided with a locknut. The head need only be a circular shell, as the bolt can be held while the locknut is tightened if a screwdriver slot is sawn in the upper screw end. The socket end should be hardened right out, with the screw stem let down a bit from dead hard.

Rockers for model engines are made in a variety of ways, being castings, machined from the solid, or fabricated from strip and rod. As a personal thing, I tend to dislike cast rockers; the only two metals readily available for castings being bronze (or gunmetal) or light alloy. Both these result in over-solid and clumsy looking items, neither metal being too suitable for withstanding bending stresses produced by sharp impact. It is not too easy to attach hardened valve contact pads to an alloy rocker in a light and easy way. On the whole, much the most satisfactory type is the mild steel strip rocker, this being quite thin but fairly deep, as results from a short length of strip used edgewise. Used in this way, it is perfectly simple to silver solder in a thin-walled central housing for a bronze bearing bush. This can run on a solidly mounted pin (or shaft, in the case of a multi) and the whole assembly is then nicely stiff against deflection in the direction in which the load will normally come.

The 1 c.c. engine features rockers where the pushrods and valve stems are not in a line square to the pivot axis. Here the rocker is in two pieces, attached at opposite ends of a short shaft running in stationary bushes. The bushes are stiffly held in a plate framework assembled on the cyliner head—quite a common arrangement. In the rocker arrangement of the 4 c.c. 4 cyl. engine, rockers No. 1 and 8 have had to be bent out at the valve end through the relative positions of valve stems and cams. This is not too good a feature, as it introduces a twisting load on the rocker. Where this state of affairs has to be coped with, it is preferable to retain a straight rocker, but provide for its angular position by setting the bearing housing at the appropriate angle in the rocker. For various other reasons this could not be done in the engine shown, so the bent rocker was reluctantly adopted. Thanks to its robust mild steel construction, it has served very well so far.

55

rocker is pivoted at its end on a ball-ended support. The support can be raised or lowered over a small range by being screwed up or down on a fine thread, thus varying the clearance under the rocker tip bearing on the valve stem. In a rocker of this sort, the hardened parts will comprise the tip bearing on the valve stem and a flat area where the cam rubs on the top surface. In a model employing these features, the two hardened areas could be separate silver steel additions, both brazed in position and hardened at the same time, as for a beam type O.H.V. rocker.

Some high efficiency car engines equipped with O.H. camshafts do not have rockers at all, but what is almost a large diameter hollow tappet. The cam rubs on the outer flat end, the outside of the cylindrical barrel runs in a machined bore in the head, while the hollow interior almost completely shrouds the valve spring and its fixing arrangements at the outer end of the stem. In this case, the "tappet" works in the inverted position compared with the conventional S.V. layout, as though it were a large thimble dropped over the top end of the valve stem and spring.

5 Cams, Camshafts, Drives

Seeing that an engine's behaviour is governed by the movements and timing of the valves, it will be appreciated that cams are of very great importance. In the early days of model petrol engines it was customary to file the cams to shape by hand, and some quite reasonable performances were obtained by cams so produced. Nowadays however, it is much more usual to machine them to shape, which results in a better finish for a start, a much more controlled shape, and a much more accurate shape.

The required movements of the valve, the kind of tappet or follower and its shape, all affect the shape of the cam, and so must be taken into account when deciding on the cam shape. The final shape of the cam too, will often decide how it can be machined accurately. These factors interact to the point where the ability to machine a cam simply and accurately to a given shape becomes the main consideration, and so influences the design of the rest of the valve gear so that maximum advantage can be taken of this ability to machine a good cam in a certain way. It is understood that this is in respect of model engines only, of course.

The design of the cylinder head and of the valves in respect of period of opening and valve lift will have been settled by the time the question of cam shape comes in for consideration, so the main features of the cam will be known. The shape of the cam has to translate these into actual movements of the valve in the most efficient way. A straightforward "harmonic" motion of the valve makes for efficient and smooth working of the valve gear, in which the valve is gently and comparatively slowly lifted off its seat, progressively accelerated during the lift, slowed down towards the top of the lift, and restored to its seat by a direct reversal of the movement sequence which lifted it to the mid-opening point. Variations and modifications to any part of the valve movement can be introduced by alterations to the shape of the cam, but these should only be considered in cases of real necessity, as they almost always result in greater stresses all round, increased wear on the valve gear and more noise.

A common and very effective arrangement is for the tappet to have a flat base bearing directly on the cam. Two major factors are involved here; the shape of the cam flank and the diameter of the tappet base. For a start it should be apparent that with a flat based tappet, the flank of the cam—i.e., that side of the cam nose that moves the tappet—must never in any circumstances be a straight line. If you imagine the axis of the tappet in line vertically with the centre of the cam, it will be obvious that there comes a point at the beginning of the lift where the whole of a straight cam flank would be in contact with the base of the tappet for an instant. This does anything but lift the tappet gently; in fact it deals the tappet a very real blow and the nose of the cam ascending at nearly its maximum speed knocks the tappet violently upwards. Such an arrangement would be intolerably noisy and

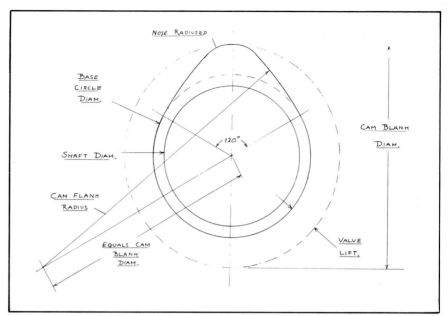

Fig. 18. Development of curved flank cam shape.

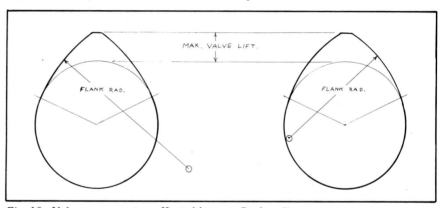

Fig. 19. Valve movement as affected by cam flank radius.

would speedily hammer itself to pieces. A gentle curve to the cam flank is required here, and the drawing (Fig. 18) showing the setting out of average typical cam curves shows what is required.

Note that the cam geometry adopted here is yet another good old British Standard Compromise. Very slight variations in the radius of curvature of the cam flank will result in a different pattern of valve movement. The drawings, Fig. 19, show but two such modifications—still keeping total period of valve opening and maximum lift the same. Decreasing the radius gives a more "humpy" curve, with a broader nose to the cam possible, giving a "dwell" at the highest lift point. The overall pattern of movement could be looked on as less smooth and "flowing" than that given by a flatter curve. Alternatively, increasing the cam curve radius and so making it more nearly flat will have the effect of producing a narrower cam nose. The valve movement here would be one of steadier speed of lift, with little or no "dwell" at the highest point. The first sort of movement given by the humpy curve could have benefits for a high speed sprint engine, where the maximum

60

volume of gas required to be passed—in or out—by the valve in the minimum time is of prime importance. Valve gear with such a cam contour would need to be very robust to stand up to the more violent and sudden valve movements, especially if this were combined with heavy valve springs for really high speed working.

The diameter of the tappet base was mentioned as the second factor to be considered in a cam arrangement of this sort. Imagining again a tappet with its vertical centre line passing though the centre of the cam, it should be apparent that the contact between cam flank and tappet base will be along a line laying across the cam flank, in line with the camshaft. This line will not always remain in the same place. When the tappet is contacting any part of the cam base circle, the line will be across the axis of the tappet. As the cam turns to bring the beginning of the lift curve into effect, so the line will begin to move outwards towards the approaching cam nose. When the cam has turned sufficiently for the tappet to be riding on the middle of the small nose radius, the line will be at its furthest point away from the tappet axis. For the cam always to contact a regular flat surface of the tappet base, the radius of the base must always be greater than the maximum distance that the contact line is displaced from the centre. This is absolutely essential, otherwise the cam nose will be scraping the edge of the tappet base, with total failure of any lubrication between the two—and very soon, total failure of the parts. This of course, is with a circular tappet base, where the tappet is free to turn. The Westbury "Dolphin" engine design employs tappets which cannot rotate, and can therefore feature bases no wider than the cam. However, in this case, as with circular bases, the cam must still be able to bear on a flat surface at all angular positions, and so this results in a rectangular base, the larger dimension laying along the line of the cam's travel under the base.

In chapter four dealing with valves and tappets, mention was made of the practice of offsetting the tappet axis in relation to the centre of the cam to promote rotation of the tappet and so even out wear. Whether this is done or not, the relationship between cam and tappet base diameter remains the same. To make doubly sure that this rotation does take place, in some car engines the cam is machined very slightly taper, and the underside of the tappet base machined equally slightly convex to match. The required action seems to result well enough in model engines with flat tappet surfaces and cam flank surfaces square to the faces.

The common and effective combination of circular flat based tappet and curved flank cam lends itself very well to all the relevant surfaces being produced by straightforward turning. The tappet machining needs no description; the procedure and jigs used in the production of cams and a complete four cylinder camshaft are detailed in "Building Mastiff", a companion volume to this one. The procedures followed there could equally well be applied to any other cams or camshaft for any other engine.

It has been emphasised that a flat based tappet can only work satisfactorily in conjunction with a curved flank cam. If the tappet base is something other than flat, then the cam flank need not be curved. For instance the tappet base or cam follower is sometimes fitted with a roller—more often seen in older engines than modern ones—in which case the cam profile can be almost any shape within reason. The cam can certainly have a straight line flank, which means that reasonable cams can be produced by filing, preferably in the lathe, making use of a filing rest. In fact it is not too easy to turn a straight flank cam in the lathe by straightforward turning. You need either some sort of copying attachment or a toolpost milling

61

spindle. In a straight flank cam, the flanks will be tangents to radii drawn from the cam centre to points on the circumference representing the valve opening and closing points. For anything like normal periods of opening, such a layout will result in quite a wide cam nose, with sharpish corners where the tangential flanks join the outer diameter of the cam blank to form the nose. All such corners need to be radiused, so as to provide a smooth transition from flank to nose. If this is not done, the tappet or follower is very liable to jump that corner on the opening side, allowing the tappet to smack back on the cam nose, producing noise and wear. Similarly the same corner left on the closing side can result in the tappet getting "left behind" as it were, for it to re-contact the flank on the closing side a little way down. This is obviously equally to be avoided.

The Westbury "Centaur" gas engine is an example of flat flanked cams using roller followers. If you can find an example of a horizontal gas or heavy oil engine, this is more than likely to feature cams and followers of this type too.

Where a roller follower is used, the surface shape of the cam flank can be even further removed from the curved shape necessary with the flat tappet, and be actually slightly concave or hollow. This results in a very fierce valve action, with the highest valve speed developed just before the top of the lift, followed by a pronounced dwell at the full open position. If such a cam shape is adopted—and it is quite unnecessary for normal purpose engines—the radii at either side of the nose need to be distinctly larger than on other shapes of cams, to take as much as possible of the "kick" out of the top end of the action.

You have probably noticed that here and there the expression "tappet or follower" is used. In this case the follower does not have to be the same as a tappet; it can be a swinging lever or rocker. The lever type arrangement is more often found in O.H. Camshaft layouts where it is essential to interpose some component between the cam and valve stem to take the side thrust produced by the cam. The same requirements apply to that part of the follower that contacts the cam as apply to tappet surfaces, so far as cam shapes are concerned. In other words, if the cam contact area on the follower is machined flat, then only a curved flank cam can be used.

In this connection it could be useful to remember that the total opening time of the valve can be altered by modification to the shape of the contact pad, without altering the cam in any way. A pad perfectly flat throughout its length will give a longer opening period than a curved one. With the curved one, the ends of the curve are further away from the circle of the cam's nose travel, and so the valve is opened later and let down on to its seating earlier; the opening time is curtailed slightly at each end. This facility has been used to operate more than one follower on the same cam, where the total opening time of one follower is not the same as the other. The example of this most frequently met perhaps, is in a motorcycle valve gear, where two followers, roughly bell-crank shaped, bear on the same single cam Fig. 20. Their contact points on the cam are arranged to occur at the right angular distance from each other, according to the valve timing requirements. The exhaust valve follower, needing a slightly longer opening period, has a slightly flatter cam contact pad, i.e., of slightly greater radius.

Incidentally, a point on cam shapes for petrol engines is that is is normal to undercut the base circle diameter behind the nose below the nominal size by the amount of the valve clearance. In the model engineer's workshop it is somewhat easier to machine the shape of the cam so that the opening and closing points correspond exactly to the timing diagram. If the base circle around the "no lift" part is then machined below size by the amount of the clearance, then the clearance will be taken up by the time the shaped cam flanks come into operation, and the valve will then lift and close at a more nearly correct time. An alternative procedure is to work out how many degrees of rotation is represented by valve movement equal to the clearance, and then add and subtract this from the opening and closing points of the cam. The first procedure tends to be easier to carry out.

It pays on the whole to keep cams and valve gear as simple and straightforward as possible, both from the designing point of view and also that of producing the actual thing. If you make any deviation from the straightforward, then you should also very thoroughly analyse the action in detail and make sure that any effects introduced by the way—perhaps at first unforeseen!—are reasonably acceptable.

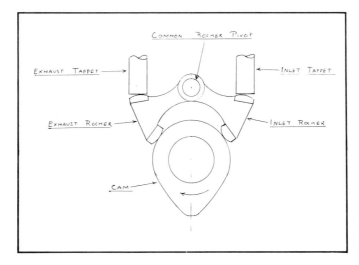

Fig. 20. Single cam operating both valves.

By way of illustration of this, consider a straightforward O.H. camshaft layout, in which the cam bears on the top of a plain rocker, the rocker in turn contacting the valve stem directly under the cam centre. If this fits in nicely in every way,— fine, no problems. However, suppose that as the design elaborates, it is decided that it would be better to locate the camshaft nearer the pivot point of the rocker, and so slightly further away from the valve stem. This will obviously turn the rocker into a lever, in which the outer end contacting the valve will move over a slightly longer arc than will the cam contact point. The next obvious thought is that to retain the original amount of valve lift, the lift of the cam will have to be reduced in the same proportion to the valve lift as the proportions of the lever. So it will,— and you can quite well lay out the cam accordingly. What is not so obvious is that you have now magnified a variable that could formerly be ignored into one that is now big enough to affect the pattern of the valve movement.

It was pointed out earlier that when a curved flank cam operated a flat based tappet, the line of contact between cam and tappet moves back and forth across the tappet base as the position of the cam varies. When the cam is operating a swinging lever instead of a tappet sliding in a straight line, this effect begins to loom quite a bit larger. When the cam contact line is nearest the valve end, the proportions of the lever give the valve the sort of action most nearly like that given by direct action of the cam on the valve stem, but when the contact line moves nearer to the rocker pivot, the lever proportions are effectively altered, so that cam movement is magnified more than if the contact line were nearer the valve. This has the effect of moving the point of highest valve lift slightly away from the mid point of valve movement.

And this is not all. Because the highest point is no longer central in the valve lift pattern, the valve will open more slowly than it closes—or vice versa, depending on the direction of cam rotation. This menas that the valve no longer has a harmonic movement, and if it is especially desired to retain this, then the cam shape has to be modified. The result is an assymmetrical cam, in which one flank is somewhat flatter than the other. The amount of correction that the cam needs can be plotted from a graph of the valve's motion over a series of small increments in the angular position of the cam; when you have this, then if the cam is to be turned on a jig, it would mean making two jigs and machining each flank as a completely separate operation. This effect actually happens in the Datsun car engine, and here the cams can be seen to have noticeably different flank curves.

Fig. 21. Building up a four cylinder camshaft from separate cams, using a simple assembly jig.

The decision as to whether the effect is worth going to the trouble to correct in a model engine is obviously one that must be left to the designer—and in view of what is involved, it may well be ignored! However, the main point in drawing attention to this detail is to illustrate how necessary it is to examine every possible aspect and the possible effect of every alteration, so as not to come up with something with an inferior performance through some slight oversight.

To return to the "workshop" aspect of cams, what about cam proportions? Well, it could be said that a reasonably proportioned cam for model engines results from making the base circle diameter about 6 times the valve lift with the thickness— i.e., the width of the flank contact surfaces—about 2 to 3 times the lift.

Regarding tappets and followers, these are both normally hardend right out (or case hardened) on the contact surfaces, and tappets can be turned from silver steel, hardened and polished. Cam followers can be fabricated much like rockers, with attached and hardened contact pads. Cams need to be hardened too, and the normal treatment given to silver steel items to be hardened right out gives quite satisfactory results.

Unless the cam followers are especially designed to work on the same cam, any engine will need two cams per cylinder. It is not too difficult to turn a single cylinder camshaft complete with the two cams out of a single piece of rod. The one big advantage in doing so is that you do not have to think of fixing the cams on the shaft at all. There can be some disadvantages. For one thing, the heat treatment necessary to harden the cams can introduce some slight distortion in the shaft part, which may not be too easy to correct. You will certainly have to clean up and polish a pair of blackened shaft journals. A good compromise is to turn the two cams in one on a common sleeve having a keyway, and to key this to a mild steel shaft—which does not have to undergo the heat treatment. Individually produced cams can also be keyed to a separate shaft in the same way, utilising some form of jig to locate the keyways in the right angular position in each.

If separate cams are to be used, then undoubtedly the easiest and most accurate assembly—particularly for a multi cylinder engine—results from the use of Loctite to fix them in position. The procedure is to make up a simple jig to position the cams accurately during assembly—Fig. 21. This technique has now been used for several engines, both multi and high speed single cylinder engines with every success.

Given the completed camshaft, it has to be driven at half crankshaft speed. The most suitable way of doing this will depend on overall design and layout of the engine.

Most model engines depend on plain spur gears for this, and there is much to be said for this type of drive. It is straightforward to carry out, reliable, and the wide range of gear sizes and pitches available in commercial stock gears means that there is very rarely any difficulty in finding gears of the right size to fit in with designed crank and camshaft centre distances. Many small commercial gears are provided with a tapped hole in the boss for a grubscrew for locking them on the shaft. The bosses are generally big enough to allow of planing a keyway through the bore, and if shaft diameters and wheel bores allow of doing this, it is always preferable to do so, rather than rely on a tiny grubscrew for security.

It may be found that the crank and camshaft centres distance is such as to result in an overlarge timing case in order to house the big wheels necessary to span the distance. Here, it is much the best procedure to introduce a third "idler" wheel between the two actual timing wheels, which will very much reduce the size of the big gearwheel on the camshaft. Some further advantages result from doing this. The idler wheel, if it is to mesh with steel timing gears, can well be of brass or bronze, which will make for very quiet running and reduce the wear on the gear train as a whole. Secondly, the shaft centres can be located just where they are wanted, irrespective of whether the distance between them can be exactly spanned by two or three wheels. The third idler wheel can be of such a size that it will just nicely mesh with the other two when located slightly to one side of a straight line between the shaft centres; in other words, slightly too big to fit exactly between the two timing wheels. This means that its bearing stud or stub axle position can be located by actual feel from the job, placing the idler gear in the correct position in relation to the other two and spotting through the bore. Lastly, the idler gear can be chosen to have a number of teeth that is not an exact multiple or factor of either of the other two. This results in what is known as a "hunting tooth", the effect being that in any turn there are different teeth in engagement at a given position than were in engagement in the previous turn. This again makes for even wear and quiet running. Suitable examples of this might be say a 24 t.

65

pinion on the crankshaft, 48 t. on the camshaft, with an idler gear of 35 t. If you have a choice between gears of similar size, perhaps from different sources, go for the thicker ones every time. These will have wider teeth that are much more robust, and will wear better through having a larger tooth contact area.

For single cylinder engines, a camshaft lying at right angles to the crankshaft and driven by skew gears makes for a neat layout. The S.V. engine Fig. 3 is so arranged. There are a couple of worthwhile points here; the 2 : 1 skew gears (or "spiral" gears) are both very small, and so can be accommodated in quite a small timing case. Both ends of the camshaft can readily be made accessible for fitting any external accessories like a contact breaker or oilpump. Alternatively, you have the choice of position for the installation of a single item like a contact breaker. Skew gears are very quiet in action, as there is a sliding action between the teeth like worm gears, rather than a face to face meeting between tooth contact faces as in plain spur gears.

For O.H. camshaft lay-outs, the shaft centres distance is generally quite considerable, and if the camshaft drive is to be all gears, then more than one idler will be required to span the distance. This is quite in order, and like the three-gear train already mentioned, gearwheel materials and sizes should be chosen with an eye to smooth running and good wearing properties. On this point of gear trains involving three or more gears, note that whatever the size of the idler wheel or wheels between the first and last gears, the size of the idlers does not affect the gear ratio between the first and last gears in the slightest. In the three gear example mentioned, using 24-35-48 t. gears, the camshaft 48 t. gear will still run at half the speed of the 24 t. crankshaft pinion in spite of the presence of the 35 t. gear. This would still hold good if the 35 were 25, 125, or the famous 57. In fact, you could include that whole collection, and you would still finish up with the camshaft 48 running at half the 24 t. speed.

On car engines, the camshaft is generally driven by chain, and this type of camshaft drive offers some attractions for driving an O.H. camshaft, where the distance to be spanned can involve several gears in a train to provide a gear drive. Properly engineered miniature chains and sprockets are available commercially, and have been used in model engines for camshaft drives. I confess to have avoided this type of drive in my own engines, largely through ignorance perhaps of how a chain might behave in running on a small high speed driving sprocket. It is possible too, in the use of chains, to strike a shaft centres distance where the chain is too tight with a given number of links, and too loose with one more inserted. In this case, some sort of chain tensioner device is called for, and this could take the shape of a "jockey" sprocket running on the outside of the free side of the chain, or else some sort of spring loaded blade tensioner to bear directly on the chain, keeping it in close contact round the sprockets. A point to bear in mind when using chains is that as the speed rises, so the chain will bow out on either side between the sprockets due to centrifugal force, and the resulting pressure at high speeds can rise to quite an appreciable value. If no sort of restrainer is fitted to the chain to control this, ample space should be allowed in the timing case round the chain so that it does not foul the inside of the case. Don't forget too, that a chain will stretch slightly after considerable use, and this will produce more slackness to be either taken up or allowed for. Where noise is something to be considered, a gear train will produce a softish whine, where a chain drive will produce a much deeper pitched roar.

Older readers who have owned or driven either Morgan or Frazer Nash cars will have very clear memories of the very distinctive chain drive noise!

in the ''valve overlap'' period—the valve overlap being that period during which both valves are open at the same time.

At about T.D.C. the exhaust gas is still moving out quite briskly by virtue of its inertia trying to maintain the speed which it attained when the piston was pushing it upwards at maximum speed. As we have just said, we can help maintain that speed a little by opening the inlet valve a shade early, and so making sure that the movement is not damped at all by the influence of the piston starting to descend, tending to draw it back. This is a ''double-edged'' effect in practice, because while the new mixture is tending to flow in through the slight movement of its own inertia, this tendency is by now quite small. Remember, the inlet valve closed three piston strokes ago, so there has been a comparatively long time elapse since the column of mixture was moving really fast—time enough for a lot of the speed to have been lost. The incoming mixture will not be accelerated again until the piston can exert some influence by speeding up on its way down the induction stroke— quite a few crankshaft degrees ahead. It therefore pays to open the inlet even earlier than would be suggested by the desire to take advantage of what movement remains in the new mixture column. At this point, the inertia of the exhaust gas is keeping it moving faster than the new mixture, so that the exhaust gas flow momentarily tends to evacuate the cylinder. If the inlet valve is opened in these conditions, the new mixture flow in can actually be assisted by the tail end of the exhaust gas flow out. This is closely tied up with what is known as the ''extractor effect'', which in conjunction with a long straight exhaust pipe can be utilised to empty the cylinder of slightly more exhaust gas than plain piston pumping would do. To take full advantage of this, the exhaust pipe length and diameter become quite critical—but that takes things into the field of high efficiency tuning, and is quite another story. So the net result of arranging a valve overlap is that the inlet valve is opened a few degrees before T.D.C., and the exhaust valve closed a rather greater number of degrees after T.D.C. See ''B'', Fig. 22.

So we can now summarise all this and translate it into a complete valve timing diagram, and see what it looks like. Such diagrams, incidentally, are always set out in degrees of crankshaft movement.

It should be understood that you cannot come up with a fixed rule and say that the exhaust valve, for instance, must always open at such and such a point. A great many things will have some bearing on where both valves' opening and closing points are fixed; type of engine, shape of combustion chambers, size of valves, intended speed, length of exhaust pipe, bore/stroke ratio and many others—almost to the point of including the time of high water at London Bridge. What we can do is to make allowance for the main features where necessary, and produce a diagram of average timing suitable for that particular engine. This again will inevitably be a compromise, and it may as well be admitted that a few degrees either way will not make a startling difference to performance, nor will they spell the difference be- tween success and failure. Past practice is often a useful thing to keep an eye on, so if we start the diagram where we started to look at valve events in detail—with the exhaust opening point—we can say for a start that it has been found of benefit to open the exhaust valve full early. While this may release a tiny bit of remaining pressure, this is not significant in amount, and is more than offset by other benefits of early opening. For one thing, there is that factor of time again. We may say that according to the diagram, the valve opens X degrees before B.D.C. In actual fact it doesn't; it *starts* to open, which in practice is a very different thing. In the valve timing diagram for a modern all-round performance engine, the exhaust valve can

69

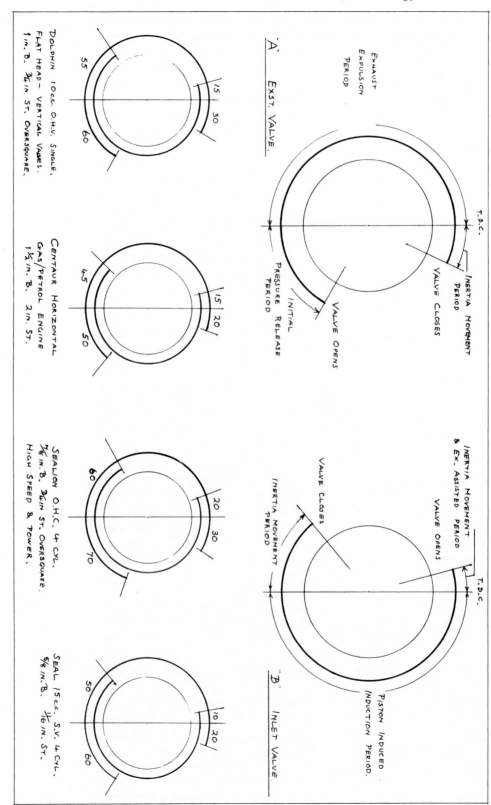

Fig. 22. Timing diagrams for various types of engines.

very well be open for a total of more than 200 deg., with the point of maximum opening around 100 degrees or more from the nominal opening point. So the piston has travelled well over half its entire stroke before the valve is fully open! In short, we can say that in a modern engine, it pays to start the exhaust valve opening anything from 40-60 degrees before B.D.C. And its closing point? Bearing the old enemy time in mind again, and that it will be nearly closed for quite a few degrees before it actually shuts off, it could be arranged to re-seat anything from 10-30 degrees after T.D.C.

Considering the same factors and the action involved, what do we settle for the inlet? While we want to take advantage of any remaining movement of the new mixture and get the valve open early, at the same time it is essential not to open it so early that the exhaust gas still has sufficient pressure and momentum to try and flow out of the inlet valve, opposing and diluting the incoming mixture. So we should be a little more cautious here and restrict the opening point to round about a maximum of 10-20 degrees before T.D.C. As for the inlet closing point, here the mixture has been positively impelled by the piston—now just beginning to move again up the compression stroke—so that its volume and recent speed mean that some inertia is in action here. Much more so than was the case when the inlet valve started to open. That means that we can take advantage of those more favourable flow features by leaving the valve closing point till later. In the case of the power stroke and the beginning of the exhaust stroke, the gas pressures involved were those generated by the combustion of the mixture, and reached quite high values. Where the induction stroke is concerned, the absolute maximum pressure that could be brought to bear is atmospheric pressure, and in practice this is never attained. So here again we cannot be too ambitious and so should let the inlet close not later than say, 50-55 degrees after B.D.C.

Assembling all these arbitrarily decided points, we come up with a typical diagram. It does not look to be too connected with hard-and-fast piston strokes, does it? That it is not, is entirely due to the fact that everything has weight and that every action takes time.

It could be said that the diagram arrived at could be suitable for an average moderate performance O.H.V. engine. Variations from this very rough engine classification could call for modifications to some of the valve timing points, and are largely a matter of common sense and some understanding of why the valves were so timed in the first place.

For instance, supposing the timing was being considered for a horizontal gas engine model, with valves in the head. First and foremost its low speed would be the biggest factor calling for modification to the timing. This type of engine is most likely to rate as a "long stroke" engine as compared with a "square" engine, in which the bore nearly enough equals the stroke. The low speed/long stroke features could therefore benefit from opening the exhaust valve somewhat later, both to extract the maximum power at low speeds and on the score of silence, the cylinder pressure being allowed to drop further before the exhaust gas is released. Gas speeds and momentum being distinctly lower, the exhaust valve could well close earlier. The inlet valve, for the same reason, could be opened later, serving to cut down the valve overlap period very considerably. The usefulness of valve overlap falls off very much as normal working speed decreases, a big overlap in such a case as this merely wasting fuel through passing new mixture straight out of the open exhaust valve if the exhaust system tends to promote this, and/or giving carburettor blow-back or mixture dilution through a too early opening inlet. The same considerations of gas

71

speed and inertia make for earlier closing of the inlet. The diagram for the Westbury "Centaur" gas/petrol engine of 1½ in. bore x 2 in. stroke illustrates these points.

By and large, the higher the speed and performance of the engine, the further the valve timing diagram can be pushed from the "hard-and-fast" stroke idea.

A side valve engine is subject to just the same timing considerations, with the proviso that by far the most sensitive spot is the valve overlap point at T.D.C. Here, the overlap should be quite small, as it is easily possible for incoming mixture to pop straight out of the exhaust valve without ever seeing the piston! The exhaust opening and inlet closing points could well be more like the moderate performance O.H.V. job, as the time factor and the more tortuous routes have a tendency to let gas speeds and inertia play a bigger part than they might in say, the slow-speed horizontal engine.

Some timing diagrams for various Westbury designed engines are shown in Fig. 22, and on considering the features of each engine mentioned, the reasons for the variations in timing can be accounted for.

So turning from valve timing to ignition timing, from the practical standpoint things generally work out very well by providing a timing adjustment control on the engine, and setting the timing in the first place so that the spark occurs at T.D.C. with the timing fully retarded. A range of advance of something like 30-40 degrees will cover normal timing advance requirements.

The fact that the timing needs any advance at all is due to the time element again. While ignition is looked on as pretty much of an instantaneous explosion, like firing a gun, it is actually an orderly burning sequence. The spark ignites a tiny patch of mixture immediately surrounding the plug points, this spreads through the rest of the mixture like a high speed prairie fire until all the mixture has been burnt. Turbulence, in the shape of high speed whirling and movement of the gas, combined with compression, very much accelerate the speed of burning as compared with the speed at which it would burn in free air, which enables combustion to be completed in the extremely short time available.

Even so, it still takes time, and the idea is to get enough of the mixture burning to produce enough heat to expand the gas to provide some usable pressure on the piston directly it is in a position to use it, i.e., at T.D.C., or very shortly after. As the burning does take a little time, we light the fire before needing to do the cooking, and so advance the time of starting things.

Different types of engines will vary in their preferred amounts of ignition advance. A high performance O.H.V. engine, for example, having perhaps a well-designed hemispherical cylinder head, could need less advance than a more "woolly" S.V. engine. When running at the same moderate speeds, that is. If you speed up the O.H.V. job to speeds beyond the capabilities of the S.V. type, then the time factor again comes into play and the performance at the top end of the speed range could be improved by somewhat more advance.

Car engines these days have the ignition timing quite precisely controlled while running by a combination of engine speed and manifold depression. I know of no model engine in which this has been done, and adding such features could well prove to have but slight benefit. It does seem a fortunate fact—in my own experience, anyway—that model engines do not seem unduly sensitive in respect of ignition advance in relation to speed variations. What suits a moderate speed seems pretty well to suit a distinctly higher speed. I have a theory about this—and model petrol engines offer unlimited scope for theories, and experiments that often prove them wrong!

The actual dimensions of a model engine are obviously much smaller than a full size one, so the distance the flame has to travel through the mixture from the plug points to the furthest point in the head is also much smaller. The time taken from ignition to final burn-out of the mixture could therefore be definitely less, so complete combustion is effected quicker.

If the ignition timing is set to suit a moderate speed, combustion takes a time suitable to that speed. When the throttle is opened, more mixture is taken in increasing the compression pressure, and the engine speeds up. The increased compression and temperature and the increased turbulence from the higher speed are all factors known to increase the flame travel rate through the mixture. This burning speed increase, in a small engine, gives the same effect as advancing the timing to start the burning earlier—which is just what is needed at higher engine speeds.

7 Conrods, Pistons, Rings

The main requirements of a conrod are that it should be strong, stiff and light in weight. Some of these factors are affected by its shape, but the metal chosen for its construction has a rather greater influence on the whole.

The production of model engine conrods is made somewhat easier by making the entire rod out of metal which is itself an acceptable bearing metal, and this normally means either bronze or dural. A bronze or gunmetal rod is perfectly satisfactory so far as bearing considerations go, but it has the disadvantages of being heavy and a little on the soft side. If the softness is counter-balanced by increasing its proportions, then you are aggravating the initial heaviness as compared with a similar size rod made from something else.

Bronze conrods generally start life as a casting, in which case they do offer a flying start towards shaping, as the shank of the rod can be cast in the conventional "I" section. This can be cleaned up quite adequately for use by simple hand operations.

Rods machined from the solid dural bar are generally all that could be desired, and are often found in small industrial engines where the loads are heavier than those in any model engine. Dural is very nice material to machine, and lends itself very well to quite precise shaping. Here, it is light enough to benefit only very marginally from being milled to an I section, and a perfectly satisfactory rod results from leaving the shank in a rectangular section. In any conrod, whatever the shape and material, all corners and edges should be rounded to appropriate sized smooth radii. It is customary to make the shank gently tapered in form, the widest part coming at the junction with the big end bearing; the various stresses are greatest here, those at the little end being almost wholly tension and compression. The edge of the shank is not always straight and often takes on a gentle curve out to the big end, something like the silhouette of a lighthouse. The size of the crankpin can play a part here, as a well shaped rod generally has a shank width at the bottom of about the same size as the crankpin diameter. In the same way, the width at the little end is generally at least as wide as the gudgeon pin diameter. To keep dimensions in reasonable proportions, the shank thickness could be looked on as round about half crankpin diameter, tapering down very slightly if required towards the little end eye.

Proportions such as these will give a rod in which the bottom of the shank immediately above the big end takes up a fair proportion of the cylinder bore at T.D.C. As the crank begins to turn off T.D.C., the bottom of the rod will move sideways for a start, and it will probably be found that this fouls the bottom lip of the cylinder barrel or liner. It is quite in order to cut out a square notch in the liner bottom edge to clear the rod, although like all the other innumerable compromises in a petrol engine, this should not be grossly big. Remember that the places where

Fig. 23. Reaming the little end bore of a partly machined conrod blank.

the cutouts will occur are thrust surfaces so far as the piston is concerned, and they take the sideways loads that the angularity of the conrod throws on the piston. They are certainly at the point where the piston side thrust is at a minimum—at B.D.C.—but even so, they should be preserved as far as possible. Well rounding the edges of the rod shank will minimise the size of the cutouts necessary.

When it comes to machining conrods, apart from getting the big and little end bores exactly the right size, the most precise operation is making sure that the two bores are parallel. This is most important, because if they are not parallel the effect is to tilt the piston sideways, which immediately introduces a lot of friction through the piston being very tight in the bore, with greatly increased wear on piston, liner and big end. The machining set-up shown in Fig. 23 takes care of this point very well. This set-up also serves to point up the desirability of machining the big end first, which gives a "datum" bore big enough to allow of mounting the rod on a fixture amply robust enough to ensure accurate machining of the little end bore. This will normally be a drilling and reaming job, where rigidity of mounting the job is called for to ensure that the little end bore is parallel through.

It is much the best procedure to set up and bore the big end in the lathe, which is normally done after all the separating of the cap and drilling for the bolts is finished. Some machinists advise using temporary bolts to hold the big end together for machining, but there would appear to be little real advantage in so doing—unless you are liable to lose one of the proper bolts! On "safety first" grounds it is preferable to use material for the bolts somewhat tougher than freecutting mild steel, and I have always found the tough socket head type of cap screw quite suitable. These are available down to 8 BA. Many years ago I had the misfortune to hit a displaced kerbstone at a fair speed in a car having wire-spoked wheels. One wheel was completely wrecked, but the salvaged high tensile spokes served as a supply of material for small bits of this sort for years! If anything of this sort is available, then you can turn up your own bolts as required.

75

Should rod material of this sort be used for big end bolts, then it pays to keep to the conventional bolt arrangement where the nut is at the bottom, bearing on the cap. This enables the bolt head to be left round, with a flat filed on the side to lock against the edge of the shank. The bolt is thus prevented from turning when running on the nut, which can be a convenience when assembling in a restricted space in the crankcase. The alternative arrangement is to have the bolt head downwards, inserted from the cap end, and screwing into a tapped hole in the foot of the rod. I tend to prefer this way myself, as it does provide a double security fixing, in that the bolt can be long enough to allow of running a nut on a stub of thread protruding through the foot alongside the shank. Not only does the nut serve as a locknut, but the bolt would still be held should the thread in the rod be completely stripped. Where the nut comes on the cap at the bottom, the nut should be provided with a lock washer. This can be merely a rectangular washer cut from thin sheet tin or shim stock, nipped under the nut, and having one end bent up close against one flat of the nut with the other end bent down over the cap edge. A hexagon head bolt inserted from below, but lacking a locknut, could be locked in the same way.

Should you turn up your own big end bolts, adjust the die to cut a thread a shade on the stiff side in the nut or rod foot; if using commercial bolts or screws and the rod foot is tapped, use a taper tap only and take it in only far enough to produce a similar slightly tight thread.

In the early paper stages of setting out a big end, locate the bolt holes as close to the bore as possible, leaving just enough metal between the bore and the nearest side of the bolt hole to avoid the risk of the bolt hole running into the bore when drilling. The overall width should be big enough to accommodate the nut or bolt head across a corner.

In the event that you wish to use a small ball race for a big end bearing on either an overhung disc crankshaft or a bolted-up full crankshaft, then the race should be a light press fit in the machined big end eye of the rod, making sure that it is pressed into position absolutely squarely. As the area of contact by any ball with its race is nearly enough a mathematical point, and it is an intermittently heavily loaded bearing, it would be better on all scores to use a needle roller race, where the area of contact is a straight line. The line contact theoretically has an infinitely greater area than the point, and so would stand up to the duty very much better. The width of the rod's big end eye should match the width of the bearing.

At the little end, the eye should be of sufficient diameter to provide adequately thick walls to the bore for the gudgeon pin. The eye is conveniently made larger in diameter in the middle than at the ends, so that the effect is one of a double taper tube; if it results in easier shaping—as by filing buttons—there is nothing against making the outside straight sided in a model rod. The smaller end of the taper shank where it blends into the little end eye can well be narrower than the outer diameter of the eye, but not less than gudgeon pin diameter.

When it comes to conrods of a metal which is not a suitable bearing metal itself, then both end bores need to be bushed. This generally means mild steel rods, having bronze bushed bores. The normal procedure for making a big end bore in such a rod is to bore the big end to bush O/D size before splitting, complete the drilling for the bolts and sweat the bush into position with soft solder. The rod end is then split, using the thinnest possible slitting saw, the cap bolted back into position and the bush—drilled well undersize in the first place—bored to size. Here the bolt holes could just nick the outer diameter of the bush, where they serve as additional

76

guards against the bush halves coming adrift and turning in the rod.

The ends of the bore in the bush need to be well radiused to clear the radii at the ends of the crankpin. If the bush ends ride on the crankpin radiused ends, you will get a false fit, with the big end being impossibly tight on bolting up.

Lubrication of the big end is most likely to be taken care of by a drilling for oil supply direct to the crankpin, so that no separate provision need be made in the rod itself. At the little end it is sufficient to drill a small hole through the top of the eye down into the bush, relying on oil mist here. The hole could be lightly countersunk at the top. Do not be tempted to drill the hole in the underside, next the shank, where it might be thought to be more in the direct way of oil fling from the big end; this will unduly weaken the slenderest part of the rod.

Those items directly connected to the conrods—pistons, are pretty straightforward. They generally take the form of light alloy castings, iron castings, dural machinings from the solid, or fabricated iron types. Alloy castings generally have a chucking piece cast on the crown and need a corebox for their production if the inside is to be fully shaped. Pistons machined from dural rod cannot be quite so fully shaped inside by machining, but can still be perfectly satisfactory and very light.

Iron castings would be produced in just the same way as light alloy ones, and machined in the same way and to the same extent. Fabricated iron pistons can be made a bit lighter than cast ones and to more uniform thickness throughout. The detailed procedure for making these, with iron rings and their heat treatment, is also set out in "Building Mastiff".

When it comes to piston rings, these could be looked on as optional on pistons from say, 5/8 in. diameter up to about 1 in. diameter. Below the smaller size their proportions make them pretty fragile, although they can be made, while above the bigger size they are that much more robust and the engine will benefit from fitting them.

For small iron pistons not fitted with rings, it is of benefit to turn in a narrow groove or two as if for rings; these trap a small quantity of oil and help to maintain cylinder wall lubrication and compression. Dural or light alloy pistons always benefit from the fitting of rings whenever possible, owing to the greater clearance necessary in the fitting of these pistons. The slacker fit of light alloy pistons shows up most when starting, when some slight loss of compression and blow-by will be evident until the engine warms up. Rings for these pistons can be made in just the same way as described, lapping a short length of bored cylinder from which the rings will be parted off as if it were the skirt of an iron piston. If a multi-cylinder engine is involved, the piston ring "pots" should be individually lapped for each cylinder bore.

Gudgeon pins can be quite simply produced from stock sizes of silver steel rod. They are normally drilled through for lightness with a hole about half the pin diameter and hardened right out. The length should be sufficiently short of the cylinder bore diameter to allow of fitting end pads of fairly soft material—brass or dural. In very small pins, suitable end pads can be made from soft copper or brass rivets, having stems of a diameter to fit snugly in the bore of the pins. Car engine gudgeon pins are often either clamped in the conrod little end or made a press fit in it, so that all the movement comes in the piston bosses, but it is more customary in model engines to take the easier course of making them fully floating; hence the need for end pads to avoid scoring the cylinder walls if the pin works along endwise.

8 Engine Balancing

The question of crankshaft balance was mentioned when talking about multi-cylinder crankshafts. The question of engine balance in general is just as important in a single cylinder engine, if not more so.

If a multi-cylinder crankshaft were tried out for balance—by rolling it on knife edges, say—it should show up as truly balanced. The same treatment applied to a single cylinder crankshaft would show it to be very badly off balance, even when it came from a smooth and obviously well balanced engine. This is because the balance weights in a single cylinder shaft have to include weights not only to balance its own unsymmetrical shape, but also to balance out as nearly as possible the weight of the reciprocating parts. In a four cylinder engine, owing to the disposition of the cranks on the shaft, the weights of the several pistons and conrods are balanced against each other in pairs, so that they pretty well cancel each other out and are automatically balanced. When the shaft itself is so proportioned that this also is balanced, then you get a smoothly running engine.

This is not so in a single cylinder engine, as there is only one lot of reciprocating parts involved, with no similar groups to set against them. These therefore, have to be balanced out as far as possible by counterweights on the crankshaft. This is yet one more compromise, as you cannot balance out exactly reciprocating masses against rotating ones, but you can get very near it. The awkwardness in doing this practically arises from the fact that with the various parts involved, some are purely rotating, others are all reciprocating, while yet others fall between the two, being partly of each type.

The moving parts that have to be taken into account apart from the crankshaft itself are the piston with its rings if any, gudgeon pin, gudgeon pin end pads and conrod. The piston, gudgeon pin and pads are obviously entirely reciprocating; the nigger in the woodpile is the conrod. The little end of this is also reciprocating, but the big end—including cap and bolts—is rotating. The best all-round balance is obtained when the crankshaft counterweights just balance all of the rotating weights plus half the purely reciprocating ones. To arrive at satisfactory values for the weights involved is not really all that difficult, but it involves a little fiddling in setting up some sort of rough apparatus to find just what they are. The two photographs, Figs. 24 and 25, show the gear that was hooked up out of scrap material to do this in the case of the 1 c.c. O.H.V. single, and give a fair idea of one way to tackle the job.

For a start, as the weights concerned are all comparisons and proportions, it is quite unnecessary to try and find out what the actual weights really are—in terms of ounces or grams, that is. This simplifies things very considerably for a start, as one can adopt something for weights which enable one to deal in quite small units, and something furthermore which is easily obtainable in the quantities required. In this

78

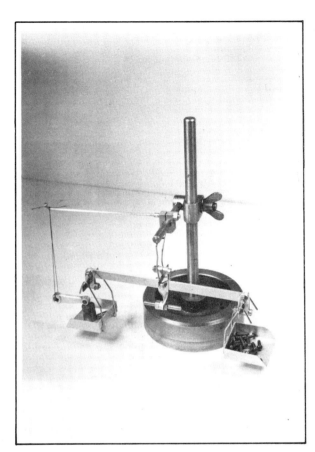

Fig. 24. Weighing the reciprocating parts of the 1 c.c. engine for balancing.

Fig. 25. Checking the crankshaft counterbalance weight, when balancing the 1 c.c. O.H.V. engine.

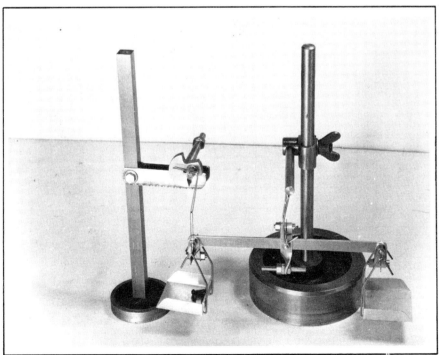

case, soft iron rivets were used, these being 3/32 x 5/16 in. One of these weighs very little, giving a nice conveniently small unit, and yet it does not take all that many to weigh as much as a small piston, for instance.

The balance itself follows the general lines of a chemical balance, and the photographs show the main features of it. The base and column were parts of an old surface gauge, while the extended arm holding the beam is merely a short length of rod arranged to utilise the column clamp that held the scriber. The beam itself and the scale pans were all cut from thin sheet aluminium. The bearing points are all more or less knife edges for the avoidance of friction, the edges being short lengths of hacksaw blade ground to a sharp edge on the back. Hanging on these, the stirrups are bent up from lengths of spring steel wire, which is quite hard. All the knife edges are held in place by clips bent up from strips of the aluminium sheet. The short length of screwed rod under the centre of the beam carries a free nut, which is used to adjust the balance of the whole thing by the position of the nut.

Perhaps a run-through of the procedure used for the parts of this engine, with the actual figures arrived at might be useful.

A start was made by establishing the total weight of all the purely reciprocating bits. These were the piston, gudgeon pin, end pads, and the little end of the conrod. Fig. 24 shows the operation of weighing these. To handle the conrod, an extra arm attachment made out of a cycle spoke was made for the balance overarm, so that each end of the rod could be weighed separately. As is seen in the photograph, the "goods" pan was loaded with the piston, complete gudgeon pin, and the little end of the conrod allowed to rest on the top of the piston, adding its weight. The big end of the rod was suspended by fine sewing silk from the extension arm. This lot weighed a total of 16 rivets. While the extra arm was in position, the conrod was reversed end for end and the big end weighed; this went 3 rivets. As it was an over-hung type crankshaft, the crankpin comes into all this, so a dummy crankpin was turned up to the dimensions of that screwed into the shaft. This was a replica of that in the shaft only to the extent of that part of it outside the crank disc; in other words, the dummy had no screwed stem, as the stem on the real pin in effect formed part of the crank. This weighted 3½ rivets.

The result of this was to provide some figures of masses to be balanced, and the sum began to look like this:

Total weight of reciprocating items   .   .   .   16 units.

As 50% of this is normally balanced,
   counterweight needed for these   =   8 units
Weight of crankpin   =   3½ units
Weight of big end   =   3 units

   Total weight to be balanced   14½ units

The next step was to find the weight of the counterbalance already formed on the crankshaft. For this, a pair of short hacksaw blade knife edges was fixed up on a column, the blades using the end holes of the original blade for bolting either side of a piece of square mild steel rod fixed to a small disc of steel for a base. The crankshaft could roll quite freely on this, and a thin wire double hook was bent up to pull on the crankpin, the business ends of the hook being straight so that they also could roll on the crankpin without causing any friction. The hook being linked to one scale pan with a loop of silk, weights were added to that pan till it was depressed to a point that just balanced the crankshaft counterweight. The operation is shown in Fig. 25. This took four rivets. So now all the information was to hand, and the sum was as follows:

Weight to be balanced . . .		14½ units
Less: Existing counterbalance weight . . 4		
Crankpin weight, as this off-sets counterbalance weight . . 3½	7½	
Weight to be added to counterbalance		7 units

The only place where anything in the way of extra weight could be added to the shaft, due to clearances, was round the outer edge of the shaft counterbalance. This was 3/16 in. thick. So a strip of 1/16 in. mild steel 3/16 in. wide was cut to an accurate length and weighed. The engine stroke being 7/16 in., the crank throw was 7/32 in. The radius of the crank counterbalance was most conveniently 7/16 in. Therefore it was reckoned that a strip of the steel weighing only half the indicated 7 units could be used, attached round the outside of the existing counterbalance, as it would be acting at twice the radius of the crankpin and so should have twice the effect of a similar weight at crankpin radius. This reduced the added weight necessary to 3½ units. From the previous weighing of the strip, this weight would be given by a piece 7/8 in. long, so a piece that long was curved to fit the edge of the counterbalance closely and sweated into position.

The result of all this was a marked improvement in the smoothness of the engine at all speeds, and a definitely higher top speed was now attainable, to the extent of nearly 1,000 R.P.M.

In the case of the engine in which this balancing operation was carried out, the valve gear is driven by a disc follower engaging the crankpin. The driven disc has two crankpin holes diametrically opposite each other for the sake of balance, the one engaging the crankpin being marked so that the timing is right on re-assembly. Had the disc been unbalanced, as it amounts to another half crankshaft, its unbalance would have had to be taken into account in the balancing procedure. However, as it was balanced for a start, it could be ignored in any question of crankshaft balance.

The operation described was undertaken to try and improve the performance of the engine, it not being known if the balance was really anywhere near right—and if not, by how much. In an engine where top performance would be of paramount importance, this sort of procedure ought to be undertaken before the various parts involved are looked on as completely finished. While it may be regarded as a fiddly and somewhat hair-splitting business, it is likely to give a far better practical result than trying to calculate all the factors involved.

To simplify it to some extent where a new engine is being dealt with, the thing to do is to make the crankshaft counterbalance as big as ever possible, and then carry out the weighing drill. If your proportions are on the right side, the counterbalance will be too big. It is then much simpler to machine off some part of it than it is to add weight to it somewhere. A too heavy counterbalance could also be lightened by holes drilled in strategic places at the greatest possible radius from the shaft centre, these having a greater effect the further they are away from the centre. A good place to add weight to the counterbalance is on its face, in the shape of a crescent of added metal—either integral or attached. Reducing the weight would

81

then merely mean taking a few skims off the face of the weight. Note that at the "on paper" stage, do not be tempted to make any such addition to the face of the weight very thick, as this will mean that the crankpin will have to be that much longer to enable the side of the conrod to clear it. The longer it is, the more leverage there is available to pressures trying to bend or break it off, and what is more, you will be adding weight in opposition to your efforts to balance things!

9 Ignition

Ignition for model petrol engines is normally by coil and battery. There is quite a choice of coils available, but not all are suitable for general model work.

Car ignition coils, for instance, can be depended on to be thoroughly reliable, but they are almost all designed for 12v. systems. This means a larger battery is needed for a start, and where the coil is one component in a system supplied by a heavy output generator as in a car, the current consumption of the coil is not of too much consequence there. The coil's current demand assumes much greater importance in model work, where it is being supplied from a battery which is not being charged all the time.

A further point against the use of a 12v. car coil is that it can perform too well. This may sound something of a paradox, but a car coil fed from a large capacity accumulator can generate a King Size spark, easily capable of flashing over the outside of the insulator of a model size plug down to earth. It also needs a larger capacitor at the contact breaker to cope with the higher voltage and heavier currents involved.

6v. motorcycle coils are generally suitable, again given a battery large enough to feed them adequately. A 4-6v. coil especially designed for model work is slightly smaller than most motorcycle types, and on the whole is to be preferred. One of these frequently to be seen advertised has served me very well for a long time now, and has given reliable ignition on a variety of engines.

Before the almost universal use of compression ignition engines for model aero work, very small lightweight coils could be obtained, but these seem to have disappeared completely. If one could be found, this would serve very well in a small boat where weight—especially of the battery—might be a consideration.

Not many people these days attempt to make their own ignition coils. The late E.T. Westbury did a lot of research and experimental design work on this subject years ago, but nothing has been done so far as I know to continue or further develop this. His efforts resulted in designs for several very small successful coils, and full constructional details were given in a series of articles on the subject which appeared in Model Engineer vols. 91 and 92 (July 1944–June 1945).

In talking about different types of coils it will have been noted that the current consumption of the coil has been mentioned several times. This is of importance, in that it affects the type and size of battery used. For reliable working at all times it is essential to have a battery well capable of supplying the comparatively heavy current called for, and one furthermore than can keep it up. Of battery types, the choice lies between an accumulator or a big dry battery. On all points, the accumulator scores heavily.

An accumulator and a dry battery on load for a period will behave in almost opposite ways. The accumulator will supply current at the amperage required

83

almost to the "last gasp", its voltage falling only slightly over the discharge period. The dry battery voltage will drop fairly steadily, together with its ability to supply the required amperage much earlier in the discharge period. If left for a while it will recover to some extent, but its ability to produce a heavy current will diminish with each period of use, until it is practically useless for ignition purposes, although perhaps showing nearly enough its rated voltage on "no load" after a rest.

For this reason it is preferable to use an accumulator for ignition every time— and the largest one that can be accommodated, if in a boat. There is the added advantage that the accumulator can be re-charged, and kept topped up by the occasional trickle charge, where the dry battery has to be discarded.

A final point to note here is that accumulators, like everything else in this world, do not last for ever. As they get older, so their efficiency decreases, and there comes a time when they cease to be able to hand out the necessary current for a reasonable time, although voltage checks show everything apparently in order.

Not so long ago I spend several days stripping down and completely overhauling two engines, neither of which would run for longer than a minute or two. It was not until a vague impulse prompted checking the age of the ignition accumulator that suspicion was aroused, when an ammeter inserted in the circuit quickly revealed the horrid truth! A new and bigger capacity accumulator instantly restored the engines to full vigour! If a very small accumulator is used, you can get this effect in a very short time through the battery's physical inability to maintain a discharge of several amps. at its rated voltage. So it will bear repeating; use the biggest accumulator possible in the circumstances.

With an efficient coil and a battery up to its job, the last item in the L.T. side of the ignition system is the contact breaker. On a fair sized engine you can often ensure that you have the basis of a good breaker by utilising commercial components intended as replacements for a car system. These can include the breaker arm, points, spring, and perhaps the capacitor. The cam you will probably have to make to suit the engine. The main drawback to this course of action is the size of the bits concerned, and the amount of room they take up when spaced far enough apart to be correctly mounted. You can get away with this with an open contact breaker easier than with one which is better enclosed—such as would be preferable in a boat where there is always the possibility of water getting in the wrong place.

To return to coils for a moment, if a 12v. coil can produce a bigger spark than is really needed, a natural thought is to run it on 6v., where the resulting smaller spark might be suitable for model plugs. The electrical characteristics of a 12v. coil are naturally designed for this voltage, and so the coil does not work with anything like the same efficiency on half the voltage. A 6v. supply also means that this voltage will only push through half the rated current for the coil, and the result of all these factors is that a 12v. coil run on 6v. produces a very feeble spark—one hardly to be relied on for dependable and certain ignition.

Without delving too deeply into electrical theory in respect of ignition coils, it should be understood that the action of the coil is in some respects like that of a transformer, where variations in the voltage and current flowing in the primary winding induce similar changes in the secondary winding which produces the spark. These changes in the primary are reproduced many times intensified in the secondary through the ratio of the number of turns of wire in the windings, the secondary having some hundreds of times more turns than the primary. Hence the spark producing voltage in the secondary is proportionately higher than the supply voltage.

84

The biggest change it is possible to produce in the primary occurs when the contact breaker points open; the current flow is suddenly cut off, the magnetic field produced in the iron wire core of the coil by the flow of primary current collapses, and the result of this sudden and drastic change is that a high intensity surge is induced in the secondary winding—this being also in the influence of the magnetic field.

However, like many other things, there are side effects produced. One of these has a bearing on the coil's behaviour at the time when the points close. When the points make contact, you get a surge of current through the primary winding. The primary reacts to this by itself behaving like a transformer and inducing its own current surge in itself, but in a direction *opposite* to that of the battery current. The result of this is that the battery current is momentarily opposed, and the induced current has to die away before the battery current can attain its full value. So when the contact breaker points close and switch on current, this builds up to the full value through the coil comparatively slowly—in terms of instantaneous happenings, that is. Which brings us directly back to contact breakers, more especially the cam.

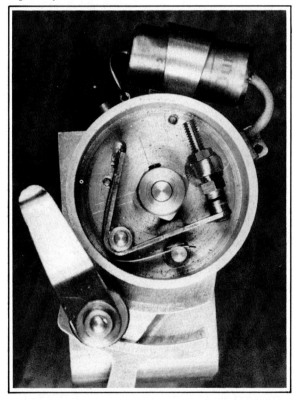

Fig. 26. A straightforward contact breaker layout, which can be made down to very small sizes.

The cam should apportion the closed and open portions of its revolution with some semblance of regard to these happenings. The period of closure of the points needs to be long enough for the full current flow to have developed, yet not so long as to drain the battery needlessly. It will be appreciated that this requirement— when considered from the point of view of actual time involved—can call for a variation in cam proportions according to the designed working speed of the engine. The cam for a single cylinder racing engine running at 6,000 R.P.M. say, could usefully use a closed period apparently much larger than that for a stationary engine running at say, 600 R.P.M. That for a four cylinder engine designed for 4,500 R.P.M. is something yet again, where it would be called on to make and break 9,000 times a minute, or 150 times a second! One can only assume that the coil manufacturer has recognised the existence of these factors, and given the coil the best possible chance by ensuring that it has an adequate period of "current on" each revolution, to let it work to its best efficiency—which again comes back to a reasonably large capacity battery.

As a rough working rule, you will not go far wrong in allowing about 90 degrees of the cam rotation for the points closed period, for a general purpose engine, that is. For a really high speed job, this could well be increased to 120 degrees or so. In the case of a four cylinder engine, you cannot do this, as there is only 90 degrees available for the whole make and break cycle for each cylinder. A reasonable compromise here is to make the points open and closed portions nearly enough equal, which cuts down the closed period to 45 degrees. The suggestion crops up from time to time that the contact breaker be mounted on the crankshaft, so that only two breaks would be needed. However, as this runs twice as fast as the camshaft, the actual times involved would be just the same!

Fig. 27. The miniature contact breaker and distributor fitted direct to the end of the camshaft of the 4.c.c. 4 cylinder engine.

The case was instanced a little way back of the contact breaker being called on to work properly at up to 150 times a second. For this to happen, the movement of the breaker arm must exactly follow the cam, just as the engine's tappets must follow the valve cams. This is best ensured by a light but stiff arm working on a free bearing of suitable materials, and a lively spring. A look at Mastiff's contact breaker (Fig. 26) shows a reasonably good way of introducing these features fairly simply.

Another useful feature of this design is that it lends itself very well to miniaturisation. The contact breaker and distributor shown fitted to the 4 c.c. 4 cyl. engine

(Fig. 27) are nearly enough exactly the same as Mastiff's, and in this case the dimensions have been successfully reduced to 1 in. dia. x 11/16 in. deep overall. The points are the same as those in the Mastiff breaker, but with the stems turned down and re-threaded 8 BA.

Contact breaker points are pretty straightforward, but there is one thing that might be said here, and that is do not be tempted to use the small silver tipped points to be found in relays. The fairly hard life that contact breaker points lead will soon burn out and wear down any softer points than the tungsten-tipped sort always used in ignition contact breakers.

Another point brought out in the breakers shown is the reversal of the normal car practice of insulating the moving point and the breaker arm from earth. This involves a flexible lead from the arm to the appropriate connection on the breaker case, and in the case of small model breakers I find it easier to insulate the fixed point. In the case of enclosed breakers, this can generally be done in a much smaller space than would be needed to house a flexible insulated lead, and any spare space here would be better used in fitting bigger and more robust points.

In choosing a capacitor, there are some electrical considerations to be taken into account. The peak voltage developed in the primary winding of the ignition coil can well reach 100 volts or more, even when the supply from the battery is only 6v. If therefore, you install a capacitor of 6 or 12 v. working rating, with the idea that this matches the battery voltage being used, the capacitor will have a very short life, either burning out or going open circuit. The proper rating for the capacitor is .1 mfd., 250 v. working.

Mounting the capacitor outside the breaker case makes not only for a smaller overall case, but greatly improves ease of replacement—or substitution by way of trial of a suspected faulty one—should this ever be necessary. If the capacitor is mounted externally, then a position for it should be provided as close as reasonably possible to the points across which it is connected. Provision should also be made for connections throughout the L.T. circuit with reasonably heavy gauge wiring, the idea being to keep the unavoidable resistance of the circuitry down to the minimum. Long thin straggly leads can cut down very considerably the amperage available at the breaker points, and this is something that could well reduce the efficiency of the ignition system as a whole.

An alternative to ignition by way of coil and battery is, of course, the use of an engine driven magneto. E.T. Westbury also did some extensive development work on miniature magnetos for home production, and the results were published in Model Engineer following his work on coil development. Like his coil researches, little seems to have been done to take this further, and while components were available commercially for building some of his magneto designs, the small demand for these appears to have resulted in the supply being discontinued.

While the basic electrical principles involved are the same in both coils and magnetos, they behave somewhat differently in use. In a coil, the battery supplies current to create a magnetic field which is abruptly collapsed to induce the high voltage surge in the secondary winding, producing the spark. In a magneto, the armature revolving between the poles of a powerful magnet acts like a dynamo, generating its own current. When the armature turns, the windings on it move out of the magnetic field cutting across them in one direction, to come under the influence of the field again in the reverse direction as they approach the other magnetic pole. This induces a peak of current in the windings, as the reversal of direction of magnetic field has much the same effect as does cutting it off in the

87

coil. In the magneto, in addition to this field reversal effect, the circuit is also broken with a contact breaker timed to break just when the induced current flow is at a maximum. The combination of these two effects produces a similar spark-producing surge of high voltage as in a coil.

Later developments of magnetos modified the construction somewhat, economising on space and improving reliability by featuring a stationary coil and having the magnet revolve between the pole pieces of the iron core on which the coil was wound. However, the effect on the coil is the same electrically.

The effects of the differences between coils and magentos is to give them different characteristics in use. With a coil, as the speed increases, so the time available for magnetic "saturation" of the core by the battery current is less, and so at really high speeds its efficiency begins to fall off. With a magneto, the opposite effect takes place, as the higher the speed the greater the current generated through the greater speed at which the magnetic field cuts across the coil windings—whether the coil is on a rotating armature or the field is induced in a stationary core by a rotating magnet. This means that a magneto is working at its least efficient at low speeds, and it has been one of the difficulties in producing a really small magneto to obtain a usable spark at low cranking speeds. At really high speeds, the magneto will produce a much more intense spark than at low speeds, and in the right circumstances, more intense than that from a coil. A big intense spark will normally ignite a bigger initial patch of mixture surrounding the plug points than a thinner feebler one, so that as the intensity of the magneto spark increases with high speed, this has led to what has been called the "self advancing" characteristic of the magneto. There is in fact no advancement so far as timing of the spark goes, but the increased effectiveness of the ignition at these higher speeds tends to produce much the same effect, as the combustion gets under way quicker from a big flaring start than from a much more modest beginning that takes longer to build up.

The lower efficiency of the magneto at low speeds can be partly offset in a rather unorthodox way. Instead of running the magneto at camshaft speed on a single cylinder engine, as the contact breaker for coil ignition must be, the magneto can be run at crankshaft speed. This immediately doubles the speed of the magneto at starting. It also produces a spark which is not wanted, but on considering the action of the engine, it will be obvious that the spare spark occurs at just about T.D.C. on the exhaust stroke—where it does nothing at all! In designing an engine intended for magneto ignition, it might pay to bear in mind the possibility of arranging the magneto mounting so that it would be driven from the crankshaft. It should also be born in mind in that case, that the magneto it is proposed to use should be capable of withstanding the maximum speed of the engine.

For those people interested enough in magneto ignition to want to try building their own, there are some points that crop up that do not appear with coil ignition where multi-cylinder engines are concerned. In a magneto having a rotating armature, the armature revolves between the two poles of the magnet, hence the direction of the field is reversed twice per rev., giving a possible two positions only when a spark can be produced. If two sparks per rev. are required, then the contact breaker will have to feature two lobes on the breaker cam to open the points twice a rev. at 180 degrees apart. This means that such a magneto can be run at crankshaft speed on a vertical twin two-stroke engine, and also at crankshaft speed on a vertical 180 degree four-stroke twin, wasting two consecutive sparks. For a vertical four-stroke twin with both cranks in the same plane, it can be run at camshaft speed. In all cases where more than one spark per rev. is required, where more than

88

one cylinder is involved, a distributor is required. In full size magnetos this is almost invariably built in to the magneto, with the distributor rotor suitably geared and timed to the magneto armature shaft. In a model, the distributor could be separately mounted on the engine, running at camshaft speed, and fed from the magneto run at a speed appropriate to the number of cylinders requiring sparks. In a four cylinder engine, this would be crankshaft speed for a magneto giving two sparks per rev.

V-twin engines are particularly difficult to equip with magneto ignition, owing to the fact that the firing intervals between the two cylinders are not equal intervals. A two sparks per rev. magneto is required, and the unequal firing interval means that the contact breaker in the magneto has also to produce unequally spaced sparks. One of the sparks must therefore be timed by the contact breaker to come in a position which is not the most efficient electrically so far as the armature position in relation to the magnet poles is concerned. This "unbalance" can be averaged out between the break points, producing two off-peak sparks instead of one good one and one much poorer. By far the best course here is to revert to coil ignition!

There have been a few engines produced—mostly vertical twin two-strokes—where both cylinders fire together. This calls for two separate sparks at the same instant, and this can only be provided by a special coil, if only one coil is to be used, or two coils both worked from the same contact breaker. If only one coil is to be used, then the secondary has to be wound especially for the job, the difference being that it must have a centre tap for the earth connection, while both ends of the complete winding are brought out as plug connections. You would probably have to wind such a coil yourself, should it be essential.

Having looked in some detail at what is involved in producing ignition sparks, we could move on to consider some of the things involved with those components that use them--the plugs.

Until comparatively recently, no-one attempted to make their own plugs as a matter of course. Various home made plugs had been produced in the past, and one way of reducing the size of these as compared with the then available commercial plugs was to make the plug merely a removable insulator, carrying a central electrode, and housed in a gland type of fixing forming part of the engine cylinder head. This did not reduce the size to a significant degree, and the size of the gap within was not too certain. E.T. Westbury turned his talents in this direction too, inspired partly I imagine by the introduction way back of an insulating material based on mica, which could be machined. The plugs so produced were successful, so far as I remember, but nothing much came of the announcement of this possibility. Various people succeeded in producing usable plugs in which the insulator was made of Steatite—which is another name for soapstone. This is a very soft, homogeneous stone, which can be machined. Plugs using this material were inevitably somewhat fragile, and these again never caught on to any extent.

Most of the attempts to produce plugs of anywhere near scale proportions were prompted by the desire to have plugs very much smaller in every respect than the smallest commercially produced plugs. The advantages for model work were several. Big car sized plugs meant that a really small engine was virtually impossible, through the necessity to house the big plug. The introduction of the 14 mm. standard car plug improved the position a little, but not all that much. The availability of 10 mm. plugs in due course was a further small step in the right direction, and indeed model engine designs are still available in which this size plug is catered for—in some cases as an alternative to the large model 3/8 in. plug.

The marketing of true model size plugs having threads of 3/8 in. x 24 and ¼ in. by 32 by several well known firms gave the model petrol engine builder reliable and reasonable sized plugs, suitable for almost every size of model engine likely to be built. These plugs made use of the same materials used in full size practice, resulting in robust and entirely serviceable plugs. Perhaps it would be truer to say "make use of" rather than "made", as they are currently available and in extensive use. The small dimensional difference between ¼ and 3/8 in. threads makes a very big difference to the overall size of the plug, so that these two sizes alone make it a simple matter to choose a plug size suitable for a given engine.

It is only necessary to refer to a plug chart, which can be seen in almost every garage, to realize the wide choice of types of plugs there are available. The differences cover reach, overall size, and varying types of points making the difference between "hard" and "soft" plugs. Purely racing plug types extend the list still further. There is no such choice with model plugs; if it takes that size, it takes that sort of plug.

While the commercially produced plugs are quite satisfactory in the majority of cases, they nevertheless do have some shortcomings. For one thing, they are made in just the same style as full size plugs, which means that they have a considerable space up around the points end of the insulator. In a miniature plug this is by no means easy to clean; indeed, if it should get swamped in neat petrol, it is not all that easy even to dry out effectively. In a really diminutive engine, this spare space represents a waste gas trap that is not always fully scavenged by the very small quantity of fresh mixture coming in. Or from the other point of view, the burnt gas trapped in there is sufficient to dilute the new mixture to an undesirable extent. It is also proportionately big enough to lower the compression ratio fractionally— especially in the case of the 3/8 in. plug.

The engine designer is going to quarrel mainly with the very short length of thread provided on these plugs, that on the ¼ in. plug being no longer than 5/32 in. When it is required to house a plug of this size in a water cooled head, it has the effect of prohibiting the water space being brought close to the plug, as the head depth there must be very little more than the plug reach so that the points can be reached by the mixture, and there has to be a completely clear area round the plug body considerably larger than the nominal ¼ in. to provide for the body size and room for a box spanner to tighten the plug. This is one case where the designer does not have a completely free hand to incorporate his own ideas—not if he is going to use that sort of plug!

It is generally the case that the larger the plug, the thicker the central electrode. This is certainly so with the 3/8 in. plug compared with the smaller ¼ in. types. It would be nice to have some small degree of choice in this matter, as a cool running engine can usefully use a thin electrode plug, the idea being that this keeps hot enough in use to keep itself burnt clear of light oil deposits. The more substantial and thicker electrode will run that much cooler; for one thing, it can better conduct away the heat produced at the gap. This may well suit a hard revving high speed engine, but might not be so generally satisfactory on a more docile engine running cooler.

It was partly the feeling of irritation and restriction with these shortcomings on the part of commercially produced model plugs that prompted the series of experiments undertaken by the writer to try and produce a home made plug that did not

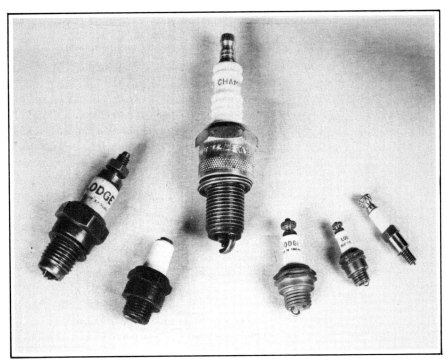

Fig. 28. Showing the progress towards really miniature spark plugs. Centre—normal 14 mm. car plug. Bottom row, L to R: early Lodge 12 mm. model plug; A.C. 10 mm. type; Lodge 3/8 x 24 model plug; Lodge ¼ x 32 plug, currently produced, and R., 4 BA home made plug.

exhibit these features, Fig. 28. A reliable plug smaller than the smallest commercial ¼ in. type was also felt to be desirable—if only because of the fascination of really diminutive engines! When it comes to designing a really tiny engine, it needs considerable juggling to accommodate a ¼ in. plug, with the necessary space round it, in an O.H.V. cylinder head. The plug has to be accessible, it must not be too heavily screened from cooling air, and you still have to find room for two valves in reasonably efficient positions.

There is quite a lot to be said for making ones own plugs. A gauge of wire can be found for the central electrode which does not exceed in use a temperature suitable for the engine in which it is to be used, and the physical size can be adjusted to be equally suitable. Where the engine is an original design of one's own, it gives one a much freer hand if the reach of the plug can be adjusted to fit in with the engine design than if the reach of the only available plug dictates one feature of the cylinder head design.

A useful and worthwhile feature of the home made plug shown is that there is no space round the insulator in the plug interior at all; the end of the insulator at the plug points comes flush with the screwed end of the plug. This not only cuts out any undesirable features in respect of pockets of burnt gas in the plug itself, but makes them extremely easy to clean.

Some photographs of Mastiff show the ¼ in. versions of these plugs fitted, while the 4 c.c. 4 cyl. baby engine has the smaller 4 BA types. All these have performed extremely well, the slow running performance of Mastiff in fact, being slightly better with these plugs than with the regular commercial ¼ in. types. These plugs in

91

the photographs have ceramic insulators, and the discovery of a readily available source of these since the publication of the original articles on making ones own plugs has resulted in a distinct improvement in the general robustness of the plugs.

As a design point when thinking about plugs, it could be well worth while to provide for the ability to fit the larger 3/8 in. plugs, if at all possible. The characteristics of this size of plug might prove to suit the engine better, when it comes to putting it into service and seeing how it behaves. If 3/8 in. plugs prove to be not too suitable, then it is a simple matter to turn up the necessary number of adaptors from 3/8 x 24 to ¼ in. x 32 t.p.i., and try the smaller types of plug. Should you do this, then bear in mind that the two types have very different reaches. The thing to do there, to cancel out this difference as far as possible, would be to make the head thickness such that the 3/8 in. plug protrudes a little too far into the combustion space, and to correct this by fitting a thick washer under the plug. Then when the ¼ in. plug is fitted via an adaptor, the points will not be too far "up the hole" for there to be much risk of misfiring. If an adaptor is used in this way, then the inner end should be coned out as much as possible to provide free access from within to the plug points. Take care not to leave any sharp edges or points on the ends of the threads.

One point which it might be useful to note here in respect of plugs in general is that if a particular engine is prone to oil up plugs, this tendency can often be cured by introducing an external spark gap in the H.T. lead to the plug. This is an old dodge often practised by impecunious youngsters in the past, when coaxing the last year or so of life out of an almost worn out motorcycle. The gap should not be less than the size of the gap at the plug points. The theory here is that the additional resistance afforded by the second gap allows a higher potential to build up before the voltage reaches a value high enough to spark over, then when it does, it goes with a splash vigorous enough to take little notice of any slight deposit on the plug points. Whatever the theory, it works! The home made plugs mentioned, having an extremely small area of insulator exposed to the actual combustion definitely benefit from this second gap in series, and will keep going even when the insulator end is visibly carboned over.

In the case of Mastiff and other multi-cylinder engines having a distributor, the spark gap naturally occurring between the rotor and the various plug lead contacts introduces this effect automatically. And this leads to a brief mention of distributors.

It might just have been possible to reduce the 4 c.c. engine contact breaker itself to even smaller dimensions, but there is a limit to how far you can go in this direction with the distributor. The limit is set by the actual distance between adjacent plug leads and contacts in the distributor top cap. This must not be so small that the spark intended for the chosen plug can flash across to a neighbouring contact and thence across the points of a plug offering less resistance than the plug under compression. Encapsulating the contacts and lead connections will not make this possible, as the rotor must be able to spin freely a few thous. clear of the contacts, and this will still provide a flash path through air. One idea put forward by Prof. Chaddock should be effective, and that is to completely fill the distributor with high resistance transformer oil. While this might well be quite effective electrically, it would inevitably introduce difficulties and complications in the way of guarding against any escape or seepage of oil via casing joints and extra bearings, and so far as I know, no-one has ever tried to produce such a distributor on a really small scale.

One relevant factor here is that this sort of oil, so far as I know, does not rate very highly as a lubricant.

The Mastiff distributor is an example of straightforward design, about which there is really little to comment. One big point to watch in any distributor is that the body and component carrying current are really good insulators. Paxolin is pretty good in this respect, and it can be readily machined. When you do come to machine it, it pays to start with a really keen lathe tool and to give this a touch-up on the stone more often than you might feel to be necessary when machining metal. Any synthetic insulating material of this sort, if it insulates against the flow of electricity it will also be a good heat insulator, hence the heat generated at the tool tip by cutting cannot flow freely away via the mass of the job, and so the tendency is to get the tool tip unduly heated. This results in an apparently abrasive action at the tool point, and if this is allowed to blunt the tool unduly, the tool starts to rub rather than cut, and the result is the generation of even more heat.

It can be seen that the distributor cap on the 4 c.c. 4 cyl. engine has individual bosses for the leads formed on the cap. This does not indicate some fancy moulding process, but the bosses were individually turned and Araldited into drilled holes in the cap. Paxolin takes Araldite very well—not all synthetics or plastics will—and this offers the designer the opportunity of building up some perhaps complex component in this material, where he might otherwise have fought shy of trying to get the shape moulded in some other material, or indeed have abandoned that particular piece of design completely.

On distributor components of this sort, it pays to get the best finish you can on them, to the point of doing a little mild polishing. If the piece is left with a rough finish, this gives a flying start to the accumulation and deposit of dirt of all sorts, and the result of this could be surface leaks of the high voltage current, cutting down the efficiency of the whole ignition system. Take a look at the inside of a car distributor cap; you will find that this is quite highly polished, just for this reason. In the case of the car component, there is generally a carbon brush contacting the centre of the rotor, and this over a long period can produce a quantity of nicely conducting carbon dust. This is one reason why it is better on the whole to avoid the use of rubbing contacts in a model distributor. Any avoidance of friction too, however small, is all to the good. Friction means wear, and if this can be eliminated, then the only destructive influence left is the erosion by the sparks on the contacts and at the end of the rotor arm. A model distributor should have a pretty long life before any corrective measures are needed as a result of this.

10 Carburation

Let us put some cards on the table and say outright that carburation on model engines is always tricky. It can throw up some problems on full size engines, and the fact that the engine is scaled down in no way scales down the carburation difficulties. These all stem from the fact that one is trying to attain an effective compromise between several different variables. Let us have a look at what is involved for a start.

The function of the carburettor is to convert liquid petrol into a gas, which when mixed with air in the correct proportions, can be burnt efficiently in the engine. The universal way of doing that these days is to use the engine's induction stroke to produce a strong flow of air through the carburettor sufficiently powerful to suck liquid fuel out of a small jet situated in the air stream, so that the fine spray is atomised in the air stream and the resulting pseudo-gas is gulped in by the engine. The air speed through the carburettor is increased by restricting the bore of the carburettor slightly in the vicinity of the jet, as the faster the air speed, the greater the suction on the jet. And here we run into the first of the compromises. If the bore is drastically reduced, then the engine cannot inspire its full quota of mixture through the inability to get the full volume of air through in time, so the engine's power is reduced through what amounts to strangulation. Resistance to the air flow can be reduced as far as possible by ensuring that the variations in bore size take place gently, providing smooth tapering approaches and exits from the constricted part—known as the "venturi". The compromise here consists in fixing sizes of carburettor bore and venturi size that enable the engine to realise its full potential, and at the same time provide air speeds fast enough to produce a usable mixture at very low engine speeds. In adjusting these factors, compromise number two is already looming up.

We have said that fuel sprays from the jet to be finely broken up in the moving air column into something like a gas. Now, petrol is many times heavier than air, and the result of this is that any variation in air speed through the carburettor results in a much larger variation in fuel output. To put it in more definite terms, if a carburettor is adjusted to give a nicely correct mixture at a given engine speed and the air speed is reduced by say, 10%, the fuel output will drop by very much more than 10%. The mixture will therefore be distinctly too weak, and will become progressively weaker at lower air speeds, to the point where, while there may still be a gentle air flow, this is insufficient to lift any petrol out of the jet at all. A simple carburettor in which this state of affairs needs to be rectified is said to be in need of "compensation". Dependent on the duties of the engine, this lack of compensation could be quite acceptable. A small aero engine for example, mostly runs at an almost constant speed and load, and given provision for temporarily enriching the mixture for starting, a basically very simple uncompensated carburettor suffices.

94

The same thing might apply to a small engine running a generator for such things as battery charging.

In full size carburettors, the throttle is generally in the form of a butterfly valve, and the first step towards compensation is to locate the jet tip near the closing edge of the throttle butterfly—or if not the jet itself, the outlet from a passage communicating with it. With this arrangement, as the throttle is closed and the space between the throttle edge and the wall of the carburettor bore reduced, so the reduced volume of air flowing through the smaller space is speeded up, and suction thereby largely maintained on the jet.

However, model carburettors very rarely feature a butterfly type throttle valve, if only because of the very small sizes of passages involved. By far the most popular type is the barrel throttle, which is in effect a plug cock, where the plug is parallel sided and retained in a blind bore in the carburettor body. The hole through the throttle barrel can then be bored so that the hole tapers outwards both ends, giving a slightly smaller bore in the middle to form the venturi. The obvious place for the jet is then right in the middle of the throttle itself, on the vertical centre line about which it pivots.

The size of the jet orifice is quite critical, and the easiest way to get it right to suit any individual engine is to make it adjustable. This is quite simply done by fitting a finely tapered adjustable needle to partially blank off the jet hole. If the range of needle adjustment is such that the jet can be closed right off or fully opened up, it stands to reason that somewhere between those extremes there must be a needle position that gives the right size of jet hole. This is always found to be so, but—and it is a big but—it is rarely the right size jet hole for all conditions of running. Compensation again!

A good many full size carburettors effect considerable degrees of compensation by means of the "submerged jet" principle. If the emission of fuel from the jet needs to be boosted in some way at the lower engine speeds, it can be done by adjusting the normal fuel level in the jet. Suppose the size of the hole in the jet is such that it can just nicely pass enough fuel for the upper end of the engine's performance, then if the flow can be kept up to some extent in conditions of lower suction, a fair degree of compensation has been introduced. This can be done by fixing the petrol level in the jet at some point high enough to cause the jet to overflow when the engine is stationary. At low engine speeds therefore, the output from the jet is not solely dependent on how hard the engine is sucking, but is partly due to the natural tendency of the jet to overflow, producing a larger fuel output than the engine by itself could induce. The fact of the jet overflowing when the engine is stationary is offset by locating the jet orifice at the bottom of a well, so that the petrol level rises in the well to the point where the float cuts off further supplies, well short of overfilling the well. This has the additional effect of providing a momentary abundance of fuel—the contents of the well—for starting up, the engine running on the jet output normally as soon as the contents of the well have been used up.

As one might suppose, jet sizes and the petrol level are quite precise in such an arrangement, and few model carburettors have been produced working on this principle. Scaling down the size of carburettor means also scaling down the latitude that you have to play with in respect of sizes and volumes, which makes for some precision work to produce a successful working model version. The "Apex Minor" carburettor by E.T. Westbury is one successful example, designed for 15 c.c. engines.

95

Further compensation can be effected in two ways—automatic or mechanical. Full size carburettors are automatically compensated, making use either of multiple jets which cut in or out as conditions demand, or else using the varying engine suction to operate some piston device to vary the position of an adjusting needle in the one main jet. Model carburettors on the other hand are mechanically compensated, there being two reasons for this. The running conditions of a model engine are nothing like so diverse as those which a car engine could be called on to cope with, and reasonably satisfactory mechancial compensation can be arranged very much more simply than can fully automatic. In fact, I know of no successful fully automatic really small model carburettor, although there are some ideas and some promising experimental results beginning to appear in this direction.

There are various ways in which mechanical compensation can be introduced, and a description of three of them may set potential designers thinking up others. To start with the method employed in the Mastiff carburettor(s), this links the needle position in the jet to throttle opening, so that as the throttle is opened for higher engine speed, so the needle is lifted slightly from the jet to provide more fuel for the greater volume of mixture required. This is done by having the throttle stalk threaded through the carburettor top cap, instead of just turning freely in it. The opposite action naturally takes place, in that on closing the throttle, the needle is moved further into the jet, reducing the fuel output.

This may seem something of a contradiction, seeing that we said earlier on that on reducing the air-flow speed, the fuel output would fall off too much. This is not so really, if things are looked at from the other end of the operating range. Imagine the engine running light at a leisurely speed on just a crack of throttle, the needle position in the jet being just right for the engine's demands. On opening up the throttle to something approaching fully open, the air flow values immediately increase by several times and the jet output tries to follow suit. However, even at full throttle conditions the needle is still partially closing the jet, and has only been raised sufficiently to permit of a controlled increase in the jet output. How much increase is allowed depends on the amount the needle is raised and its degree of taper. The amount of lift is fixed, so the best results right through the range can be arrived at by slight adjustments to the length and angle of the needle taper. This is something that can only be finally settled by trial, deducing from the engine's performance what alteration is required and in which direction. It can be a patient business—but if you want a really nice performance, there is no dodging it with any carburettor!

The carburettor shown fitted to the S.V. engine in Fig. 3 introduces mechanical compensation in a different way. Here, the degree of compensation is adjustable over a very wide range, and like jet size, somewhere between the extremes must be the right combination of all the factors. The difficulty is in pinning them down!

This carburettor has in effect two throttles, one either side of the venturi in which the jet is situated. The jet has the normal needle adjustment, not only for adjusting the jet size to a basically suitable value, but for the ability to richen up the mixture temporarily for starting. The throttle nearest the engine is the normal throttle that any engine needs, controlling the quantity of mixture inspired by the engine. The outer throttle is just like the inner one, but serves only to control the quantity of air sucked through the carburettor. It will be obvious that if the engine is running at a fixed speed with the throttle set, the effect of say, closing down the outer throttle slightly will be to restrict the quantity of air and so enrich the mixture. The mixture would naturally be weakened on opening it up. To control the richness of the mixture at varying speeds, the quantity of air admitted needs to be controlled by the engine throttle position, and this is done by the linkage between the two throttles visible in the photograph.

The angle of opening of the air throttle is controlled by the degree of opening of the gas throttle, but the attachment point of the link on the gas throttle is adjustable. Thus, if the link pivot point is fixed on the gas throttle closer to the bearing than it is on the air throttle, moving the gas throttle will have less effect on the air throttle. In other words, the air throttle will be swung over a smaller angle than the gas throttle. This effect is made use of to shut down the air throttle only slightly for a much bigger degree of closure of the main gas throttle, which has the effect of only slightly enriching the mixture as the main throttle is closed. In addition, the length of the link is also adjustable, so that one throttle can be opened or closed more than the other to any extent, before either throttle is moved. This sets their basic relative positions for a start. With this arrangement it is possible to find settings such that the mixture is progressively enriched as the main throttle is closed, to exactly the right degree that suits the engine. This arrangement works very well—in one given set of speed and load conditions. There are also atmospheric conditions taking a hand, and on first getting the settings just right, it was found rather troublesome to get a good start and clean running next day if the weather had changed considerably overnight! The high degree of sensitivity of the various differences and combinations of settings for consistent good results made this a tricky carburettor to get just right at any one time, but when you did get it right, it was good.

The third method of compensation is demonstrated very well in the carburettor designed by E.T. Westbury for his "Seal" 15 c.c. 4 cylinder engine. Here a normal barrel throttle is used, but the jet is arranged horizontally underneath the carburettor body, with the jet orifice coming just about on the vertical centre line of the throttle. The jet is fitted with the conventional adjusting needle and a small hole in the jet housing admits air across the top of the jet, connecting with a hole in the bottom of the throttle. As the engine sucks, so air flows in at the small bottom hole, picks up a rich mixture from the tip of the jet, passing this up through the bottom of the throttle barrel and into the venturi. Here it is diluted with incoming air through the venturi, down to an amount that produces a usable mixture. When the throttle is closed down somewhat, the amount of plain air passing through the venturi is restricted, and so the suction on the tiny air hole by the jet is increased, enriching the mixture fed into the air stream.

Full compensation is effected in this carburettor by adjustments to the shape of the entry and exit ends of the venturi through the throttle barrel. To enrich the mixture at small throttle openings for instance, the engine side of the venturi hole is slightly enlarged on the closing edge, so that when the throttle is nearly closed, the air entry side is nearly enough fully shut, while there is still a crack of opening left on the engine side of the throttle. This tiny opening serves to transfer practically all the engine suction to the mixture hole in the bottom of the throttle, as there is insufficient opening on the air side of the throttle to admit enough air to dilute the neat mixture from the jet very much. So the mixture is distinctly richer than at larger throttle openings when more plain air is admitted. This sytem works extremely well, and a carburettor of this sort has given good service on several different types of engine, and has been made in several different sizes. The adjustments to the edge of the venturi hole are quite critical, and the recommended procedure is to make an enlargement of the hole in the form of a small notch filed in

97

the closing edge of the hole concerned. If things are overdone, then a similar smaller notch has to be made in the opposite end of the venturi, cancelling out the effects of the too large one to some extent. Like almost all miniature carburettor tuning, it is a patient business of making a very slight adjustment and trying it out, doing things a very little at a time, and doing only one thing at a time.

It was said a little way back that model engine duties do not call for quite the same degree of versatility so far as carburation is concerned as do car or motorcycle engines. This was—and is—true for the majority of small engines in use. However, with the advent of model petrol engines being used for things like passenger-hauling model diesel locos, the need is beginning to arise for something better in the way of carburation; something that more nearly duplicates the car engine's ability to tackle varying loads at different speeds merely by operation of the throttle. This calls for a carburettor much more fully "automated" than the majority of plain adjustable needle types now in use. It is quite easy to think up conditions of use where the present carburettors fall down rather badly in use. For instance, suppose a model diesel loco is powered by a small scale petrol engine that can normally handle the load. By dainty manipulation of throttle and perhaps jet and/or air control, the load is got away and worked up to normal speed. The loco now encounters a slight up gradient on the track. The effect of the increased load will be to drop the engine revs. The effect of the reduced engine speed *at the same throttle opening* will be to reduce the air flow speed, and so the suction on the jet; so the mixture weakens— just when you can do with it enriched, if anything. Mechanical compensation cannot help here, as this comes into operation as the throttle is closed, keeping the mixture reasonably constant over varying amounts of throttle opening. When the

Fig.29 Some model carburettors. Top L. mechanically linked "twin throttle" type. Top R.—Westbury "Seal" air-bleed compensated type. Bottom L.—Seal type, with adjustable air bleed; Bottom R.—experimental fully automatic carb.

engine speed drops under load, the impulse is to open the throttle still further for more power. This you will not get with the plain mechanically compensated carburettor, as the compensation is directly linked to throttle opening, and any other set of varying conditions immediately takes the engine's requirements outside the carburettor's ability to supply. Several of the types mentioned are shown in Fig. 29.

So there is a wide open field for a lot of interesting experimental work in producing a simple minature fully automatic carburettor. The need has hitherto been very small—but it is growing.

So, given that you want to design a carburettor for a given engine, what sizes do you make things, and what proportions are likely to produce results? This entirely depends on what sort of engine it is, and what you want it to do. It pays here, on the whole, to think more of the slow speed end of things, rather than the flat-out conditions; on everything other than a purely sprint engine, that is. Nice slow speed running means a readily controlled engine, and one that will be a good starter. The top end of the speed range can, to a considerable extent, be left to look after itself in my experience. It all comes down to a question of air speed—and you can get an awful lot of air through a comparatively small hole in a short time when there is a pound or two of pressure behind it. For a normal kind of engine, a fairly safe rule is to make the main bore through the carburettor about 25% of the cylinder bore. Where you want some top end performance, this could be increased to some 30% without too much falling off at the bottom end. For the all-out racing job, something like 1/3 should be looked on as a reasonable maximum.

Note that these proportions also apply to the ports and passages from the carburettor to the inlet valve. In most cases the exhaust passages can be as big as you can accommodate, unless you are doing some fancy tuning by way of exhaust gas extraction.

And what about the proportions of venturi restriction to the main bore? Well, here again it depends on a number of things. It is common, in high speed racing two-stroke practice, to have near enough no restriction at all, relying on the extremely high air speed through the carburettor to do all the fuel lifting required. For myself, I find that a 10 degree taper at each end of the bore through the throttle barrel gives a nice gentle "in-and-out" through the venturi, so I drill the bore well undersize for a start, then enlarge it from both ends with a 10 degree taper D-bit till both ends of the hole are nearly enough the same as the main bore. In a small diameter throttle this gives a very slight constriction, but just enough to ensure that the most is made of the air flow through. Note that here, if you are intending to introduce mechanical compensation by way of adjusting the sizes and shapes of the ends of the throttle bore, you can get off to a flying start by making the bore ends of unequal size. In other words, you can run the D-bit in slightly deeper at the engine end of the bore than at the air entry end, so enlarging the exit end slightly more than the entry.

In any experimental alterations of this sort, it is really essential to make the slightest possible alteration at a time, and to try it out each time before going any further. With the very small volumes of air and petrol involved, a very slight alteration can make a big difference to performance. And to repeat, alter only one thing at a time, or you will lose the state of affairs where things were tolerably satisfactory and finish up with little idea of what it was you did that made the big difference.

With so much depending on the relative volumes of petrol and air flowing through various sized holes, it might be thought that much would depend on the

99

Fig. 30. A convenient fuel and ignition supplies arrangement for running an engine on the bench. In this case, cooling arrangements omitted for clarity.

petrol level in the jet in static conditions. To a considerable extent this is so, but in practice it will most likely be found that it is of less importance than first thoughts might suggest. When a very elementary jet system can lift and spray something as heavy as paint, you realise that the extremely small "head" represented by say, an inch of petrol, is in fact an infinitesimally small pressure, in view of the lightness of petrol compared with some other fluids. It is not of course, a head caused by the supply being higher than the jet that has to be considered, but just the reverse—a lift of those proportions that is involved. In practice it will generally be found that the suction at the jet is quite capable of lifting the petrol the odd inch or so once the engine has got going, and that a drop in the level of something like that much during a run through the fuel being used up makes very little difference to the engine's performance.

Many small stationary engines used for running small generators have a low-mounted petrol tank, where the engine is required to lift the petrol all the time. Where this is the case, it can cause the engine to be an apparently reluctant starter, as it has to be spun over a number of times to suck petrol up to the jet for the initial start. The usual practice here is fit a "foot valve"; that is, a light non-return valve in the rising fuel line so that once the fuel has been lifted to the jet, the supply pipe remains full for a considerable time after the engine has stopped. This ensures a ready start next time.

This can obviously be applied to a model engine, but a somewhat easier system is that shown in the bench running arrangement, Fig 30, where the petrol is given the initial lift to the carburettor by gently blowing into the "tank" before any attempt is made to start the engine. Once the engine has got going, it can look after itself.

In the very early days of car engines, the petrol tank was generally installed on the bulkhead behind the engine, some inches above jet level. Now the tank is

100

Fig. 31. The Mastiff flat four engine again. It is shown here in the single carburetter version. The carb. is horizontally mounted, feeding the two manifolds via the long curved induction pipe.

almost invariably rear mounted, with a pump feeding fuel to the engine. Both these arrangements feed fuel to the carburettor in free-flowing quantities far too much for the carburettor's requirements, and in the case of pump-fed fuel, at some pressure. Car carburettors have therefore always incorporated a float feed arrangement that meters the petrol fed to the jet, so that the fuel level is maintained just below the jet outlet. This also results in the degree of suction required to lift petrol from the jet remaining constant.

Plenty of model carburettors have been made with float feed, but probably many more without. The basic idea is that the supply is cut off at a pre-determined level by the float, generally operating a needle shut-off valve. The principle is exactly the same as that of a domestic water tank. Car carburettor floats were generally of very light gauge brass, but now more often of plastic, operating the needle either direct or via a lever. Model carburettor floats are generally shaped from a block of balsa wood, varnished with something impervious to petrol, like shellac varnish. This seems a little difficult to get now, but some of the modern proprietary varnishes are petrol proof. With a small float such as would be employed in a model carburettor, the pressure it can exert when floating is not all that great, so rather than have the needle operated direct by the float it is preferable to "gear down" the action by a light lever to multiply the pressure available. If this is done, a neat arrangement results from making the lever in the form of a bell-crank, with a side entry for the fuel supply near the top of the float chamber. One advantage of this is that the float and needle action can be watched with the top of the float chamber off, which cannot be done if the supply pipe connects to the middle of the chamber lid.

There needs to be some degree of adjustment available to the level at which the

101

float shuts off, so as to be able to get the level right in relation to the jet. In a direct operating system, where the stem of the needle passes through the centre of the float, this is arranged by providing several alternative positions on the needle for the spring clip against which the float pushes. Many direct operating car type floats push straight on the end of a stub needle; here the sizes and proportions are correct by virtue of the manufacturers' construction, so that a similar system in a model carburettor would necessarily have to include provision for adjustment. With the side entry arrangement, you can either bend the long arm of the bell-crank that contacts the float, or make the needle valve housing in the float chamber adjustable as to position, screwing it further in or out to vary the shut-off point in relation to the height of the float. When establishing a new design of carburettor utilising float feed, it is as well to get these proportions fixed before making the final connection arrangements between float chamber and carburettor body, or you may find them so positioned that the float cannot cut off the supply at a low enough level.

Examples of carburettors can be found—both in full size and model practice—mounted horizontally or vertically, the vertical mounting generally being described as the "downdraught" position. Originally this style of mounting was adopted for cars for the sake of the small amount of extra acceleration it was said to give, the idea being that gravity helped the engine suction to inspire the mixture. Everything is subject to the effects of gravity, and the atomised petrol present in the air constituting the mixture adds to the weight of the air to form in effect a heavier-than-air gas. So advantage was taken of this to utilise the effect of gravity on the mixture to help the engine take in the maximum amount of mixture at full throttle conditions. As acceleration is not very often a factor taken into account in the design of model engines, the very slight advantage that the downdraught mounting of a model carburettor might confer over one mounted horizontally is of doubtful benefit. The twin carburettors version in Mastiff's system as seen in Fig. 30 were vertically mounted merely as a matter of convenience and space-saving; this position gave a very simple throttle linkage layout and simplified the dual petrol feeds. Fig. 31 shows the single horizontal carburettor version.

If a model carburettor is vertically mounted, a point to watch is to ensure that it does not easily overflow, as any fuel discharged from the jet when the engine is not running will go straight down into the manifold in the case of a multi, or straight into the inlet tract if a single. This could not only make the engine reluctant to re-start after a stop, through upsetting the mixture, but would introduce an undesirably large amount of neat fuel directly into the cylinder, possibly diluting the cylinder wall oil film or wetting up the plug(s). In full size engines, where a downdraught carburettor is fitted, the manifold is invariably fitted with a small bore drain pipe, through which excess neat petrol can drip away before being taken into the engine. This must necessarily act as a tiny extra air inlet, but the volumes of air involved in car carbuation are large enough for carburation not to be upset by this. The manifold drain is not normally fitted in models; carburation there is already touchy enough, without adding any more factors to be taken into account!

102

11 Lubrication

Lubrication is all important in a petrol engine, and ways of getting oil to the components that need it must be taken into consideration right from the earliest stages of the drawing board work. Rather surprisingly perhaps, while the supply of oil is essential, it is sometimes something of a problem to supply it in small enough quantities.

A great many really old full size engines worked on the "total loss" principle, in which a small quantity of oil was continuously supplied, sufficient to balance the engine's consumption. My first motorcycle had a hand pump built in to the front end of the petrol tank, a partition in the tank serving to allow the front end to act as an oil tank holding about a quart. One gave the engine a pumpful every five miles or so in normal running. If ascending Porlock or maybe the Spittal of Glenshee, then one gave it an extra one for luck! In spite of this very hit-and-miss system, those old engines performed very well and lasted for years. At least, mine did. Early model engines featured very similar lubrication arrangements, in some cases with a spring-loaded pump feeding through a needle valve, so that a small supply was maintained all the time. Unless you remembered to shut off after a run, "all the time" meant while the engine was stationary, too!

An alternative to the total loss system in really old engines was the arrangement of an oil trough under each big end, the big end caps being provided with a small scoop, the root end of which communicated with a small hole drilled into the big end bearing. On every rev. the scoop dipped just under the surface of the oil in the trough, forcing some oil into the big end bearing. It also served to fling a fair amount of oil around in the crankcase, lubricating pistons and cylinder walls. There were a number of drawbacks to this system; one was that at the higher speeds, the big end scoop tended merely to cut a groove in the oil, which had insufficient time to re-form into a pool before the scoop came round again. It tended also to produce a lot of oil froth, which while being generally reasonably effective as an oil supply, did make an engine so equipped run very "wet". Many engines, in fact, whose oil supply was arranged in this way, featured baffle plates at the base of the cylinder to keep some of the oil out of the cylinders. These plates shut off the bottom open ends of the cylinders as completely as possible, having merely a narrow slit cut across the middle through which the conrod swung. The "Seal" 15 c.c. engine has this system, which appears on the whole to be quite satisfactory. However, where there is a fair chance of the engine being tipped around somewhat—as in a boat—I would prefer to see some rather more positive way of feeding oil to the points that require it, combined with some measure of control over the movement of quantities of contained oil.

Modern car engines now have their own built-in supply of oil, this being circulated in fair quantities and returned to the sump at the bottom of the crankcase

103

by gravity. A good many model engines work the same way, Mastiff being a case in point.

The total loss system is still quite a sound propostion especially when the design caters for metering the oil to the engine in appropriate quantities. The design points arising here are: what means can be adopted to get the oil to where it should go, and where should it go?

Let us first think about means of pushing the oil around. In single cylinder engines it is easy. The piston, in moving up and down the cylinder is for three of its strokes, acting as a simple pump. The underside of the piston, in moving the air contained in the crankcase is also acting as a pump—or trying to, and when the air is totally enclosed the piston merely compresses this air on its down stroke and allows

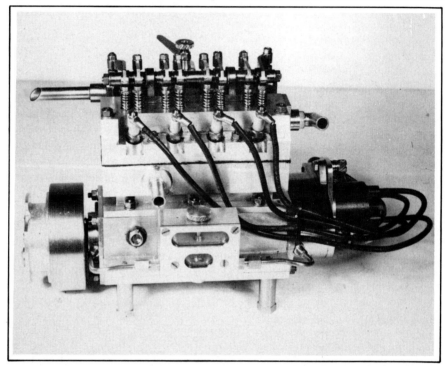

Fig. 32. Oil tank and lubricator fitted to the 4 c.c. 4 cyl. engine, worked by displaced crankcase air. Left of the tank can be seen the crankcase air non-return valve.

it to re-expand on the up stroke. This action can be put to good use by utilising the varying pressure in the crankcase to pump the oil. It can be done in two ways. Either the crankcase can be fitted with a non-return valve so that the air is displaced from the crankcase, creating a depression that can be used to suck the oil into bearings or wherever, or the pressure created in the crankcase on the piston down stroke can be applied to a separate airtight oil tank, forcing the oil to where it is wanted. Either system works quite reliably, there being the slight disadvantage in the pressure system that any slight seepage of pressure through crankshaft bearings or elsewhere tends to make for a messy engine, as oil will inevitably be blown out with any escaping air. The suction system on the other hand works the other way, and tends to keep an engine free of oil outside, as any air movement is inwards into the crankcase.

104

It is quite surprising how effective an air pump the engine piston can be, used in this way. In the S.V. engine shown in Fig. 3, the small cylindrical object to be seen immediately behind the contact breaker is the oil tank, while the machined boss on the timing case cover is the air non-return valve. This is a plain disc type, and the pin retaining the disc is clearly seen. On first trying out the engine, the oil tank was about three quarters filled, and after a few minutes running the workshop was filled with quite a visible blue fog, not to mention a smell. The oil tank was found to be completely empty! Steps were taken to cut down the rate of flow to a fraction of this amount, on which quantity it has run happily ever since. In the 4 cyl. engine shown in Fig. 32, the oil tank is a diminutive affair, milled from a solid block of dural. Two deep grooves were milled in the face of the block, the longer top one being the tank proper, and the lower one the receiving half of a sight drip feed. A shaped cover plate clamping a celluloid window on the face of the block allows the action of the drip feed and the quantity of oil remaining to be watched. The filler cap screws in the top and is so shaped to act also as a needle valve, allowing oil to drip into the bottom chamber where crankcase depression sucks it via the two side pipes into the crankshaft main bearings each end of the crankcase. While the capacity of the tank can be measured in drops rather than fluid ounces, this quantity is quite sufficient to satisfy the engine's needs for much longer than it has ever run at any one time.

It is pretty obvious that a single piston moving up and down its cylinder can act as a pump, but it may be nothing like so clear how four pistons, two moving up while two similar ones move down, can produce the same pump effect. At first thought it would seem that the two pairs would cancel each other out, so that any air displaced by the two descending pistons would merely occupy space created by the other two ascending. This is in fact what mainly does take place, but there is nevertheless a definite pumping action displacing air from the crankcase, if this is free to escape. While it is not too easy to explain how this comes about, the diagram Fig. 33 may help to make things clear.

When a piston is at T.D.C., the conrod and crank throw lie in one straight line; when it is at B.D.C., the same thing applies. Therefore, when the piston is halfway down its stroke, the conrod and the crank throw will stand at 90 degrees to each other. Now, this is *not* a half turn on the crankshaft, because when the crankshaft has turned 90 degrees, the crank throw will be horizontal. Therefore, the piston has reached its half-stroke position before the crank has done a half turn. Suppose these conditions apply to pistons Nos. 1 and 4 in a 4 cylinder in line engine. While Nos. 1 and 4 are reaching their mid-travel point coming down, what is happening to Nos. 2 and 3? Why, they are approaching their mid-point travel going up. So, when 1 and 4 reach their halfway stage, with the crank having turned only 80 degrees say, 2 and 3 will be well short of their halfway point going up, as the crank has a further 20 degrees to turn before 2 and 3 reach their halfway point. Therefore at half stroke, 1 and 4 will have displaced half the total volume of air that they will move, while 2 and 3 are a long way short of having made room for it—so air is driven out of the crankcase if it is free to escape. The same thing will happen again when the ascending pair of pistons come to descend in their turn. This effect is admittedly reversed further round the stroke when the "short halfway point" applies to the other pair of pistons—but then it is too late! If the air has been displaced from the crankcase via a non-return valve, well—it just cannot return, so you create the slight crankcase depression in the 4 cylinder engine that can be used to promote oil flow.

A moments thought will show that this effect is more pronounced with short

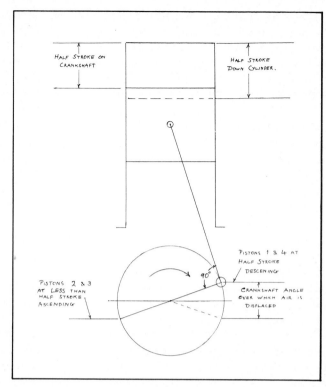

HALF STROKE ON CRANKSHAFT

HALF STROKE DOWN CYLINDER.

PISTONS 1 & 4 AT HALF STROKE DESCENDING

90°

PISTONS 2 & 3 AT LESS THAN HALF STROKE ASCENDING

CRANKSHAFT ANGLE OVER WHICH AIR IS DISPLACED

Fig. 33. How crankcase air is displaced in four—cylinder in line engines.

conrods than with longer ones, through their greater angularity to the vertical at half-stroke.

The bigger the engine, the bigger the volume of air displaced, and this is why all car engines have a crankcase breather fitted somewhere. In the case of the 4 c.c. 4 cylinder engine shown, this effect is still there, although extremely small due to the tiny pistons with their very short stroke. The effect is so small in fact that it has really insufficient time to operate at highish speeds, with the result that the oil flow virtually ceases, and the engine has to be throttled down to a tick-over for a few seconds before the oil drip can be seen to have picked up again. A case of the effect of time and inertia again!

As a final point on oil circulation systems using a crankcase non-return valve, the discs in the disc valves I use are made from thin Paxolin, and work very well. They are in fact very similar to those used in car petrol pumps. They seat on a flat seating machined with a square-ended D-bit. The discs are quite small, the largest being about 3/16 in. diameter. Sheet Paxolin has a smooth well finished surface, so no grinding-in or other seating operation is required. I evolved an easy way of making these, with a truly turned edge down to as small a diameter as you may want. In fact, I make them from copper laminate board, which is Paxolin sheet with a very thin layer of copper deposited on one side. This normally has a total thickness of about 1/16 in. The dodge is to chuck a stub of brass rod, face the end flat, and then turn down the outer 3/16 in. or so to slightly smaller than the finished diameter of the required disc. An oversize roughly cut disc of the laminate sheet is then sweated centrally on the faced end of the brass rod, the copper face being tinned quickly with a small iron. The stub is then rechucked and the piece of sheet turned to size, using very light cuts with a keen lathe tool. When down to size, it is unsweated off the rod, the copper face wiped clean while hot, and that is that. The disc seats

106

Fig. 34. 1/8 in. bore oscillating cylinder oil pump fitted to an early experimental flat-four engine.

Paxolin side down on to the seating. Sometimes the copper facing will come unstuck from the Paxolin on unsweating from the chucking rod—in which case you can use either side as the seating side.

To return to the matter of crankcase pressure in 4 cylinder engines, is someone about to raise the point of how the Mastiff flat four behaves in this respect? Yes, . . well here, as the two pairs of pistons are opposed and therefore behaving exactly alike so far as travel and crankshaft angles are concerned, there is no air displacement at all to be considered. That is, in theory. In practice, there may well be a very slight build-up of pressure due to expansion of the air contained in the crankcase for a start when things warm up, not to mention any minute piston blow-by that could conceivably occur when starting from cold. In Mastiff, this would be free to escape via the drain holes into the timing case, and thence to the outside from around the starting dog. Any such slight movement would convey oil mist to the timing case; what you might call turning an unwanted factor to good account!

It was partly for the reason that crankcase depression could not be used here that an oil pump was fitted. Rather than have a separate oil tank and run the engine on the total loss system, it is much simpler when an oil pump is fitted, and the engine is big enough to accommodate a pump, to arrange a full flow system, diverting the major part of the pump's delivery back to the sump through a pressure relief valve, following full size practice.

Note that an oil pump does not necessarily have to be one of the meshing gears type. A reciprocating pump such as an oscillating cylinder model loco lubricator pump is quite in order, and in fact an old model B.S.A. motorcycle engine used an oscillating cylinder oil pump. An experimental 10 c.c. flat four engine built by the writer some years ago used such a pump very successfully, and the arrangement of

107

this is shown in Fig. 34. A pump of this sort needs to be run much slower than a gear type pump, and in this case the pump was driven by home-made worm gears from the crankshaft nose, geared down 15 : 1. It was anticipated that the engine would be able to take all the output from such a tiny pump running at a slow speed compared with the engine speed, so no relief valve was fitted. In the event, this proved to be wrong, as when the engine got going, it was necessary to stand well clear of the fine oil spray coming off the back of the flywheel! A pressure relief valve was therefore fitted in the external oil piping, affording a return of surplus oil back to the crankcase. This resulted in a rather makeshift looking arrangement, and illustrates the necessity of providing for such things while the engine is still only on paper. However, one lives and learns, and that misjudgement enabled a similar thing to be avoided in Mastiff.

One method of supplying an engine with oil has not been mentioned, because it is very rarely seen. This is the petroil system, which is now normally confined to two-strokes. Here, a measured small quantity of oil is added to the fuel and in the case of two-strokes, as the mixture enters the crankcase, the oil comes into contact with and is deposited on cylinder walls and all the moving parts in the crankcase. This works very well, but is not as a general rule applicable to four strokes. There was one exception though, in which it was successfully applied to a four stroke, and that was in the Morton 5 cylinder radial aero engine. Here the individual induction pipes were brought down and led into the crankcase, with the carburettor attached to the crankcase and feeding into it. This enabled the moving parts in the crankcase and the pistons to be lubricated just as in two-stroke practice, but I have no knowledge of how the timing gears and cams fared. I would have expected these to be somewhat starved, as none of these parts would be anywhere near the direct path of the oil-laden mixture from carburettor to induction pipe.

So having looked at ways of persuading the oil to go places, where is it going?

The most highly stressed bearing in an engine is the big end. If therefore, an ample supply of oil can be arranged direct to the big end, the escape of oil from that bearing will ensure that enough is flung off to look after the needs of the cylinder walls, the little end and the gudgeon pin. The usual way of feeding the big end is through drilled holes in the crankshaft, the crankshaft inlet hole being located in one of the main bearing journals and lining up with a hole in the bearing through which the oil is fed. Should the crankshaft bearing be a ball bearing, then a similar result can be arranged through an additional bearing sleeve on the shaft, especially for the oil feed. A little way back it was said that metering the very small amount of oil necessary was sometimes something of a headache. When you consider the minute length of time for which the two holes—one in the shaft and the other in the bearing—are in line, and for which the oil can flow when the engine is running briskly, this is very far removed from a free and unimpeded flow, and goes a long way towards the desired metering. Even with small plain holes, it is easily possible to pass too much oil through these for the engine needs, and so the shaft should never be necked nor the bearing grooved out with the idea of making the oil available to the big end throughout the whole of each crankshaft revolution.

With the oil supply under gentle pressure, either from crankcase pressure or from an oil pump, the oil present under pressure during the time the big end feed in the shaft is blanked off is ample to lubricate the shaft itself in its bearing. In fact there will be an escape of oil from this bearing in just the same way as the oil escapes from the big end. Just as the big end oil escape is used to lubricate the piston, so oil escape from the crankshaft bearing can be utilised to lubricate the timing gears.

When talking to people about this sort of thing, and the operation of drilling the crankshaft for oilways is mentioned, listeners have been known to look a bit startled—if not horrified. There is nothing really to be feared in this operation, and it is quite straightforward even with a four-throw crankshaft. If the shaft is clamped to the vertical slide with the table set 90 deg. to the faceplate, the angle and position of holes drilled from the chuck can be accurately controlled. The tiny crankshaft for the baby 4 cylinder engine was drilled in this way for positive oil feed to all four big ends via the two end bearings, and the whole job went through quite smoothly. Incidentally, particularly with single cylinder engines, a gravity oil feed to the big end via the crankshaft is often quite effective, as the oil present in the big end bearing will be flung out through centrifugal force. If there is a further oil supply present in the crankshaft oilways to make up this loss, the result is a gentle oil feed independent of any pressure. If such a system is adopted, then it would be as well on starting the engine for the first time, to provide a little gentle pressure for a few moments to ensure that the oil does reach the big end for a start. If there is none there, it cannot be flung out to start the flow.

Model engines mostly have a lot of things exposed that are enclosed in full size practice—and I am thinking here mainly of valve gear. Rockers, bearings, valve guides, push rod ends, valve stem ends—these are all enclosed in a car engine and in most cases have their own individual oil supplies arranged. This is not always possible in a model engine, and the engine having all these things exposed with no positive oil supply generally leads a tolerably happy life by making do with the occasional attention with the oilcan. This is acceptable so far as it goes, but if things can be improved in this respect it is only reasonable to do so. Overscale plugs can be a stumbling block to completely enclosing an O.H.V. head, and unless it can be enclosed, a force-feed oil supply to points on the head becomes a doubtful possibility. Like oil feeds to big ends and crankshaft bearings, there is going to be a continuous oil escape, and with nothing in the way of enclosure built in, this becomes virtually uncontrollable.

In a car engine—to draw the comparison once again—the enclosing rocker box is in direct and free communication with the crankcase. Indeed, oil is generally poured into the crankcase via the rocker box. If this feature can be arranged in a model engine, then it is unnecessary to provide any separate oil feed to components in the rocker box, as these can be sufficiently lubricated by oil mist from the crankcase. If, in addition, a crankcase breather is provided on the box itself, then the air displaced from the crankcase will have to emerge via the box, and the transfer of oil mist into the box made that much more positive. Total enclosure of pushrods can be something of a problem, but if this can be arranged neatly with comparatively large bore tubes, these can serve to convey the oil mist. There is one slight snag here—if it can be looked on as a snag; there is then nothing to see working!

In a single cylinder engine it is a conventional arrangement for the timing case to be cast as an extension of the crankcase. Where this is so, the back wall of the timing case is the timing side wall of the crankcase, and so the camshaft bearing in this dividing wall between crankcase and timing case can be plain bush, open both ends. In this case, that camshaft bearing will automatically receive oil through being open to the crankcase. This is not the case with the front one however, where the camshaft may well have to protrude through the timing case cover for the contact breaker mounting. To look after this, and to make sure that the cams themselves get their ration, the timing case back wall can be cut away considerably to provide as free a passage as possible for oil mist from the crankcase into the timing

109

case. This needs to be done with some discretion, of course, as this partition is the housing for both a crankshaft and a camshaft bearing. This also applies to a timing case in which the camshaft lies at 90 degrees across it, being driven by skew gears. With this arrangement, it makes for a clean engine to make the bearing at the end of the camshaft not carrying the contact breaker a blind bush. This can tend to run dry, and it is a worthwhile point to drill a tiny oil hole in the top of the bush to encourage some oil to find its way in. The most certain way to ensure that all shaft bearings get oil of course, is to arrange a positive supply, as in Mastiff.

The oil pump on Mastiff follows car engine practice in that it is driven at camshaft speed. In the light of experience in running this engine, the oil pump could well run somewhat slower than this, maybe half its designed speed. In the design of this engine, it is very convenient to drive the pump by the same shaft on which the contact breaker is mounted, and this merely means that the pressure relief valve bypasses more oil than it would with a slower running pump. Where a drive at that speed is far the best way of doing things, then the pump could be made slightly smaller, when its output would be correspondingly reduced.

Modern engines tend to be conspicuous by the absence of external oil pipes, the necessary passages being drilled through the appropriate places in the main engine castings. This is a worthwhile example to follow—with limitations. It might be advisable to avoid a really deep drilling where the end of the hole must exactly meet another hole, or finish up really accurately in an exact spot. Model engine castings for the most part being in light alloy, there is always the possibility that a deep hole may wander slightly and either miss its exact destination, or be sufficiently off course to only partly connect with the other hole, which can result in a very much restricted passage which would be very difficult to correct. The deep drilling stands a very much better chance of being successful when it is aimed at something comparatively large, such as a bearing bush or other large diameter hole. Where such a drilling is deemed to be acceptable at the design stage, then matters can sometimes be improved or made that much more certain by shaping the pattern to include the rib on the casting in line with the drilling, so providing plenty of room for the drilling—and any slight deviation of it from the intended line. This is the sort of point that should come in for consideration at the stage two drawings.

And talking of things that should be considered at the design stage, bear in mind that small drills such as might be used for oil feeds, are not all that long. It is quite possible to find, when you come to drill such a deep small hole, that before you can do so you have to make your own spear-point drill, merely to have one long enough to cope. This comes back to the "availability statistics" mentioned in the first chapter on design in general. As a case in point, the oilways through the Mastiff crankshaft are just about the limit in depth which could be drilled with the diameter drill mentioned. One sometimes sees advertisements for job lots of extra long small diameter drills; when these are of usable sizes, it always pays to get a few just for such jobs.

One last point crops up from time to time on this question of oil, and that is the oil itself. What is the most suitable type? It has been suggested that something like Redex might be suitable, as being thin enough for small mechanisms and having good penetrating properties that would ensure it getting to all the places needing it. This would be much too thin bodied, in my opinion. When used as an upper cylinder lubricant in car engines, its penetrating properties and "creeping" ability serve some useful purpose when added to the fuel, in serving to lubricate the inlet valve stems where the heavier engine oil, working down from the top in small

110

quantities, could soon get washed off by the incoming mixture—especially in rich mixture starting conditions.

For model petrol engine work I personally use Castrolite, which is 10-30 multigrade oil. This is somewhat thinner than that normally used by most car engines, and therefore more suitable for the smaller components and loading encountered in model engines. No doubt any similar viscosity oil of reputable make would be equally suitable.

Incidentally, just to mention it in passing, I also use this in the lubricators of my ML7, where it appears to be quite satisfactory.

As a final thought, a fault-finding table has been included at the end of this book. This is not to imply that it is thought that anyone running model petrol engines might not be able to trace any troubles that might crop up. However, some of the causes are not always all that obvious, and a list of possible causes of misbehaviour might well save time when something more obscure than the straightforward occurs, and the perhaps unsuspected cause does not spring readily to mind. Most of them have happened to me at one time or another—but they all help you learn a bit more about petrol engines!

Fault Finding Table

FAULT	POSSIBLE CAUSE	REMEDY
Engine will not start	Almost anything!	Check systematically through for: choked jet; choked fuel line; lack of fuel; ign. battery in order; good connections throughout; breaker producing spark; plug clean; jet needle free; engine not flooded with fuel or oil.
Starts—splutters to a stop, but *will* re-start	Jet needle closed too far	Open up slightly.
	Partially choked jet	Disassemble and clear.
	Partially choked fuel line	As above.
As above, but will *not* re-start	As above	As above
	Plug oiled up or fuel-soaked.	Clean; try different plug.
	Throttle lever loose	Check and re-tighten.
	Fuel leak starving carb.	Check and re-tighten unions.
	Disconnection in ign. cct.	Check and re-make connection.
	Wire broken	Test through circuit with meter or battery and bulb.
	Plug lead moved and sparking to earth	Re-position; check spark at plug top while working breaker by hand.
	Cont. breaker sticking.	Clean and free out.
Runs briefly O.K., then dies.	Insufficient fuel or obstructed fuel line	Replenish; clear fuel line.
	Almost discharged ign. acc.	Re-charge.
	Almost exhausted ign. dry battery.	Renew; exchange for accumulator.
	If old or untried batt. or acc., not big enough capacity	Replace with new or larger.
	Oil reaching breaker points.	Clean; rectify oil seepage.
	Plug oiling up.	Check and clean plug; check amount of oil reaching plug; check oil quantity in engine; introduce external spark gap at plug top.
	Valve stem sticking on warming up.	Check comp. directly engine stops, testing valve's free movement with finger tip; disassemble and free.

FAULT	POSSIBLE CAUSE	REMEDY
Runs briefly O.K., then dies.	Insufficient fuel or obstructed fuel line	Replenish; clear fuel line
	Light alloy piston too tight partially seizing.	Check resistance to turning by hand when hot; disassemble and free.
	Piston ring tightening on warming up through too small gap	Check as above and enlarge gap.
	Dry bearing somewhere tightening on warming up.	As for light alloy piston.
Runs sluggishly; no revs., no power	Air leak in induction system	Check by blanking off jet, blowing or sucking at air inlet. Re-make joints or tighten unions. Check throttle fit.
	Valve improperly seating	Listen for leaky valve on turning slowly over comp. by hand; grind in very lightly.
	Open cct. or burnt-out capacitor	Substitute to check; replace if faulty.
	Ign. too far retarded	Check for slipped timing; re-set and advance.
	Valve timing slipped	Check timing, re-set and lock.
Persistent or violent misfire	Mixture too rich	Modify fuel feed level. Shut down jet needle slightly.
	Intermittent short to earth or break in wire	Check with meter or batt. and bulb while moving wires.
	Plug lead moving and sparking to earth occasionally	Secure well clear of engine and/or earthed components.
	Internal elec. leak in plug.	Discard and replace.
	Loose contact somewhere	Re-tighten all connections.
	Sticky or tight contact breaker arm	Disassemble, clean and free out if necessary.
	Loose contact breaker point	Check and tighten.
Sudden loss of compression	Plug worked loose	Re-tighten with new washer.
	Valve sticking open	Check for blow-by with wet finger over ex. pipe or carb.; disassemble and free
	Tappet loose and unscrewing	Check as above, re-set and lock.
	Piston ring partly gummed up	Disassemble and free.
Sudden loss of compression, if after hard run.	Hole burnt in L.A. piston crown	Fit new piston.
	Valve stem warped, holding valve open.	Replace valve.
	Carbon flake stuck on valve seating.	Clean, preserving good seating surface.

113

Index

Ignition —
  accumulator, 83
  capacitor, 87
  coil, 83
  contact breaker, 84
Interference Fits, 32

Liners — cylinder, 34
Little End, 76
Loctite, 20, 31, 33, 40, 65
Lubrication, 103

Magneto —
  multi cylinder, 89
  principles, 87

Oil —
  pressure relief valve, 110
  pumps, 107
  types, 110
  ways, 109

Patterns —
  coring out, 20
  cylinder head, 35, 39
  simple, 18
Petroil Lubrication, 108
Pistons, 77
Piston Rings, 77
Plugs —
  home made, 89
  location, 37
  reach, 90
  types, 54
Ports, 42, 53
Pump — oil, 107
Pushrods, 55

Rockers, 55

Shrink Fits, 32
Silver Soldering, 57
Skew Gears, 66
Sparking Plug — see "Plugs"
Starting, 28

Tappets —
  bases, 59
  offset, 54
Timing —
  valve, 67
  ignition, 73
Timing Case —
  development, 16
  oilways, 109
Total Loss Oil System, 103

Valve —
  bounce, 51
  clearance, 62
  follower, 17
  foot, 100
  grinding in, 53
  guides, 40
  lift, 53
  machining, 48
  material, 47
  non-return, 106
  overlap, 71
  rockers, 55
  seats, 40, 54
  springs, 50
  stems, 48
  timing, 67